TIME COUNTS

THE STORY OF THE CALENDAR

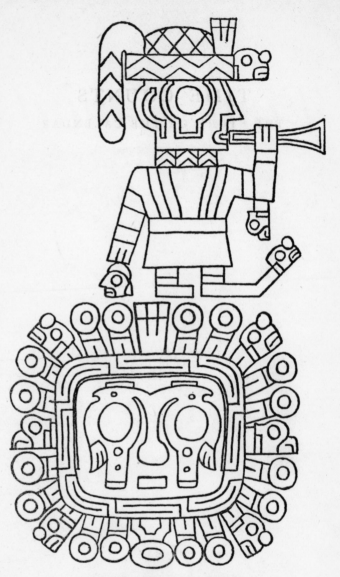

PREHISTORIC CALENDAR ?

Detail from sculpture on the ancient monolithic Gateway of Kalasasaya (facing page 72) near Tiahuanaco in the Bolivian Andes. A modern theory suggests that the Gateway is of immense age and that its sculpture records a Calendar 'before the Flood'. According to this theory the section shown is the 'fourth Twelfth' coinciding with one of the Equinoxes, and every detail of the figure has calendrical significance. Although the theory is not accepted by astronomers, it supports the probability that there were calendar problems countless centuries ago. (See Part I, Chapter I: 'Before History')

Time Counts

THE STORY
OF THE CALENDAR

By
HAROLD WATKINS

Foreword by
LORD MERTHYR
Chairman, British Advisory Council
of the World Calendar Association

PHILOSOPHICAL LIBRARY
NEW YORK

Published 1954
by Philosophical Library, Inc.,
15, East 40th Street, New York 16, N.Y.

Printed in Great Britain for Philosophical Library by
Barnicotts Limited, Taunton, Somerset

List of Contents

Part 1

Part 2

CONTENTS

Part 3

Illustrations

Calendar Tables

Acknowledgments

A BOOK that sets out to be an historical record, however inadequate and incomplete, must depend on many references to the work of others. This one is no exception. Therefore I put on record with most grateful thanks my indebtedness to numerous authors and publications. In the text of the book and in footnotes I have given where I could the sources of my information.

Especially I wish to thank Mr. H. S. Bellamy for permission to use his interesting book, *Built Before the Flood* as the basis of my first chapter, and his publishers, Messrs. Faber & Faber; Dr. Mildred Fairchild, for quotations relating to the Soviet calendar experiments from *Factory, Family and Woman in the Soviet Union*, which she wrote in co-authorship with the late Dr. Susan M. Kingsbury, and also Messrs. G. P. Putnam's Sons, who published it; Mr. C. A. Kincaid, for extracts from an article on the Indian calendar in the *Journal of the Royal Asiatic Society*; Professor R. Levy, of Cambridge, for extracts from his book on *The Persian Language*, and his publishers, Messrs. Hutchinson; Professor Aspinall, of Reading, Mr. W. S. Haugh, City Librarian and Elizabeth Ralph, City Archivist of Bristol, all for their friendly assistance in connection with the famous "Give us our Eleven Days" disturbances in 1752; Mr. H. St. John Philby, for an extract from his fine biography of King Ibn Saud, and the publishers, Messrs. Robert Hale; the Royal Statistical Society for permission to use their Library and consult their Journal; and to the Astronomer Royal, Sir Harold Spencer Jones, from whose pamphlet on the history of the calendar I have quoted, and who is also one of the oustanding advocates

ACKNOWLEDGMENTS

of reform. I am particularly indebted also to Dr. Bhola D. Panth, of Teachers' College, Columbia University, for the many extracts I have made from his brilliant study *Consider the Calendar*.

If in this list I have omitted to give thanks where they are due, it is not from lack of gratitude, but rather space, and I proffer no less my thanks.

I would express my obligation to those who have given me personal assistance, notably Mr. S. J. Noel-Brown, F.A.I.A., and Mr. H. Kenneth J. Watkins, A.C.A., for their information on the practical applications of the calendar to industry; and to Mr. J. Harrington, for his collaboration with me in preparing the index. Finally, I must put on record my deep indebtedness to Miss Elisabeth Achelis, Founder of the World Calendar Association, to whose kindly encouragement and support this book largely owes its inception; to Mr. C. D. Morris, dynamic editor of the *Journal of Calendar Reform*, from which I have so largely quoted, and whose personal encouragement has also been continuously inspiring; to Mr. James Avery Joyce, honorary secretary of the British Section of the Association, for his unfailing encouragement and valuable criticism; and, last but far from least, to Lord Merthyr, who has kept the cause of calendar reform alive in Britain over many years, and as head of the Association in this country is giving so distinguished a lead to the campaign for this long-delayed but urgent reform. In particular I offer him my sincere thanks for sparing time from his busy public life to write a foreword to this book.

HAROLD WATKINS.

London, *November*, 1953.

Foreword

THOSE ENGAGED in the long struggle for calendar reform are aware that they have many obstacles to overcome before they achieve success. A conviction that they will eventually succeed is the spur that keeps the movement going, and gives it vitality. We do not underrate the difficulties; and we know that the greatest of these are apathy and ignorance.

Mr. Harold Watkins has performed a valuable service by writing this book. Fresh minds approaching the problem need to know something of the history of the movement from its earliest times; and I am glad to find that Mr. Watkins has dealt fully with the story, particularly that part which relates to the last two centuries.

I earnestly hope that Mr. Watkins will be rewarded by a quickening of interest in this matter amongst all English-speaking peoples. These should surely set an example to the rest of the world; and it is discomforting to find that it is they who have so far failed to do so. There are, moreover, too many people who dismiss calendar reform as the machination of cranks, or as a proposal incapable of being universally accepted.

Let no one suppose that there is anything impossible about it. What is required is a spirit of goodwill and compromise on all sides, unimpeded by political or selfish considerations. There are, we know, genuine critics, for the most part on religious grounds, whose views are worthy of examination and study. Mr. Watkins' book will do much to make the issues plain, and I sincerely hope that it will be widely read.

MERTHYR

November, 1953

Introduction

1

IN ONE OF those famous *Letters to His Son* written by
that polished courtier and wit, the fourth Earl of Chesterfield, to instruct the young man in good manners and to
impart to him the essentials of knowledge, the Earl more
than once refers to Chronology. 'It is very necessary', he
says, 'that you should know something of it', and then
he goes on to define chronology as 'the art of measuring
and distinguishing time, or the decline of epochs, which,
you know, are particular and remarkable periods of time'.

To such a statesman concerned with world affairs an
'epoch' may have offered a reasonable unit of measurement, but it would seem now somewhat broad, as well
as indefinite. However, an epoch is very much a matter
of time, and only by its measurement in years can we
give it an appropriate place in the scheme of things. His
lordship went on to outline the various 'eras' on which
all our time records since the beginning of recorded
history have been based.

The Greeks measured their time, he states, by Olym-
piads, which was a space of four years. This method of
computation, he then explains, 'had its rise from the
Olympic Games, which were celebrated the beginning
of every fifth year, on the banks of the River Alpheus,
near Olympia, a city in Greece. The Greeks, for example,
would say that such a thing happened in such a year at
such an Olympiad: as, for instance, that Alexander the
Great died in the fourth year of the 114th Olympiad'.

1

So that his son might get this information into right
perspective, the Earl added that 'the first Olympiad was
774 years before Christ; so, consequently, Christ was
born in the first year of the 195th Olympiad'.

He coupled chronology with geography. These are
called, he said, 'the two eyes of History, because History
can never be clear and understood without them. History
relates facts; chronology tells us at what time they were
done; and geography shows us in what place and country
they were done'.

'There are two great periods of chronology', continued the Earl, 'from which the nations of Europe date
events. The first is the Creation of the World; the second
the Birth of Jesus Christ. Those events that happened
before the birth of Christ are dated from the creation of
the world. Those events which have happened since the
birth of Christ are dated from that time: as the present
year 1739'. Then he sets out these examples:

	A.M.
Noah's Flood happened in the year of the world ..	1656
Babylon was built by Semiramis, in the year ..	1800
Moses was born in the year	2400
Troy was taken by the Greeks, in the year	2800
Rome founded by Romulus, in the year	3225
Alexander the Great conquered Persia	3674
Jesus Christ born in the year of the world	4000

and, further to clarify the young man's mind, adds: 'The
meaning of A.M. at the top of these figures, is *Anno
mundi* the year of the world', but, 'from the birth of
Christ, all Christians date the events that have happened
since that time; and this is called the *Christian era*.
Sometimes we say, that such a thing happened in such a
year of Christ, and sometimes we say, in such a century.
Now, a century is one hundred years from the birth of
Christ; so that at the end of every hundred years a new
century begins; and we are, consequently, now in the
eighteenth century'.

Thus the youth was introduced by his scholarly and sophisticated parent to the calendar, and it is an illuminating sidelight on the trend of the education of the period to note the items in the calendar which that worldly nobleman picked out as the further outstanding events of history:

Mahomet, who established the Mohametan religion, and writ the Alcoran, which is the Turkish book of religion, died in the seventh century, that is, in the year of Christ　　..　　..　　..　　..　　..　　632

Charlemain was crowned Emperor in the last year of the eighth century, that is, in the year　..　　..　　800
Here the old Roman Empire ended.

William the Conqueror was crowned King of England in the eleventh century, in the year　..　　1066

The Reformation, that is, the Protestant Religion, begun by Martin Luther, in the sixteenth century, in the year　　..　　..　　..　　..　　1530

Gunpowder invented, by one Bertholdus, a German Monk, in the fourteenth century, in the year　..　　1380

Printing invented, at Haerlem in Holland, or at Strasbourg, or at Mentz in Germany, in the fifteenth century, about the year ..　　..　　..　　1440

The noble Earl, for all his learning, would seem to have been a little indefinite on one or two of these items, and to have got them out of proper chronological sequence, which is odd, but he was well illustrating the essential purpose of chronology and the calendar. Also, either by design or coincidence, some of his selected dates were far from unconnected with the history of calendars. It is interesting that his lecture, though contained in a not particularly lengthy letter, as letters in those days went, should cover so extended a period—a period which is, in fact, all of historical time. No documentary or graven history takes us farther back in time than the 4000 B.C. which Chesterfield noted as 'the creation of the world', with one possible but much disputed exception—the Calendar Gateway of Tiahuanaco.

Therefore no calendar, as we understand the word in its physical sense, can take us back over more than the 5,953 years which have passed since that traditional and literally epoch-making date.

But some sort of calendar for checking off the days, the seasons and the years, was among the earliest inventions of man, and we can trace it back through most of that time. At first it was rough and ready. Time has done much with it, in more senses than one, but it is still imperfect and inadequate. Today the world uses a number of different calendars and none of them is perfect. Perhaps the absolutely perfect calendar is impossible, but what we have could be improved.

What we have is the Gregorian Calendar, so called after Pope Gregory XIII who, in the sixteenth century, introduced to Christendom certain modifications of the older Julian Calendar. That had come down from the days of Julius Cæsar and was in use by what is broadly described as 'European' civilization. It was a calendar which divided a year of $365\frac{1}{4}$ days into twelve months of varying length. That is, it was a solar and duodecimal calendar. Other calendars were in use in other parts of the world. India and China had their different systems. The Persians had theirs; the Egyptians and the Abysinians and the Japanese. The Incas and the Aztecs had curiously complicated systems of counting time and the days. In a general way it can be said that there have been almost as many calendars as religions. They still are numerous. India, for example, has more than a dozen different calendars in simultaneous use today.

But gradually the Gregorian calendar has become the more or less universal time system for civil, international and commercial purposes. England adopted it two hundred years ago, Japan in 1873, China in 1912, Turkey in 1916, and Russia after her great revolution in

1917. Other countries at other times. Revolutions have several times in history been responsible for calendar as for other reforms, though not always successfully. The French revolution produced a most ingenious decimal calendar which might well have been to time reckoning what the metric system is to weights and measures, but after a few years it was abandoned.

Time has always been a difficult thing to measure. It has been described as a flow, but differing from other flows in that everything flows with it. At best its measurement is relative—even the pendulum will swing at different periods at different places on the earth's surface —but science has evolved methods of measurement which are satisfactory for all practical purposes, down to tiny fractions of seconds; at the other extreme the astronomers deal in light-years and parsecs[1] with ever increasing accuracy. Only the year itself still suffers in its accepted and everyday measurements from obsolete and antiquated calculations and divisions. After 370 years the Gregorian calendar is out of date, and calls loudly for reform, though that does not make the calendar story less interesting. As Chesterfield was at such pains to explain to his son: chronology, and therefore the calendar, is history.

But this chronology has given historians a great deal of trouble. Over the centuries law, custom, tradition and religion have all taken a part in adjusting dates to events. New Year's Day, for example, has slipped up and down the calendar. It has been for its various purposes, religious or secular, December 25, January 1, March 1, March 25, Easter (moveable) and September 1. As, instance, when in Italy in the Middle Ages:

If we suppose a traveller to set out from Venice on March 1, 1245, the first day of the Venetian year, he would find himself in 1244 when he reached Florence; and if after a short stay

[1] A parsec is equal to 3·20 light years.

B

he went on to Pisa, the year 1246 would already have begun there.

Continuing his journey westward, he would find himself again in 1245 when he entered Provence, and on arriving in France before Easter (April 16) he would be once more in 1244.[1]

Much later than that we had in England our own internal date confusion, for up to the year 1752 there had long been two calendar systems in use: an historical and a civil reckoning. The civil year began on March 25, but for historical purposes the start of the year was accepted as January 1. 'Thus', as Whitaker puts it, 'the Civil or Legal date 1658 March 24, was the same day as 1659 March 24 Historical; and a date in that portion of the year is written as: March 24 165$\frac{8}{9}$, the lower figure showing the Historical year'. To complicate this still further, in the last 170 years of this period, i.e., between the introduction of the Gregorian calendar on the continent, and England's acceptance of it, the English and continental calendars differed by first ten and then eleven days. Thus a date like January 5 1740 in London was December 24 1739 in Paris or Rome. From a European point of view, the problem lasted, moreover, into what is practically contemporary history for it is only a few decades since the countries of the Orthodox Church came into line—Yugoslavia and Rumania in 1919, and Greece in 1923.

2

The day is the most obvious and simple unit of time measurement—or seems to be. A day is a day whether it is a Monday or a Sunday or called by any other name. And its principal characteristic of alternate daylight and

[1] Reginald L. Poole, *Medieval Reckonings of Time* (S.P.C.K., 1921).

dark repeats itself in regular cycles. The moon is another obvious, though larger, unit. It goes through its series of four phases with apparently perfect regularity. The seasons, too, arrive in a consistent sequence. And there is also the sun, which seems to follow a strictly regular pattern that again repeats itself over a certain (rather larger) number of days.

These are the natural elements of the calendar. To complicate it—as though it were not complicated enough—we mark off the days in groups of seven, calling the groups weeks. The seven-day-group, however, does not fit exactly into the observable variations of the moon, the sun or the seasons, although there are reasonable approximations, as in the length of four weeks compared with the four-part cycle of the moon, or one lunation, and 52 weeks with the return of the sun to the same place in the heavens. The sun's return, however, seems to coincide accurately enough with the cycle of the seasons, and the fact gives us another unit. We call it a year, and find that it occupies 365 days—or thereabouts. But twelve lunations also agree roughly with the sequence of the seasons, and that can be called a year also, although the whole twelve occupy a total of only 354 days—or thereabouts. Both series have been, and are, regarded as years for calendar purposes.

Now the lunation, or moon-cycle, is not an exact number of days, but occupies just over $29\frac{1}{2}$. The division of the year which most nearly corresponds to it is called for convenience a month, and for the purpose of a lunar calendar that is approximated at 29 or 30 days alternately.

A twelfth part of a 365-day year is also called a month, but this again is approximate and varies in length, in terms of days, from 28 to 31. Both kinds of year, therefore, whether totalling 354 or 365 days, are divided into 12 months.

In only one case will the weeks fit exactly—that is when the month has 28 days, which occurs only in the 365-day year and then only once: in February, though that does not happen every year, for February is extended once in each cycle of four years to adjust the year to 366 days.

The 354-day year is the basis of the lunar calendar; the 365- or 366-day year the basis of a solar calendar. Both types are widely used, as is also, to a less extent, a luni-solar calendar, which is a combination of both. Our own calendar, the Gregorian, is of the solar type; that of the Mohammedans the lunar; the Jewish system is luni-solar.

The making of the calendar is essentially a function of the astronomer. Civil calendars are convenient approximations to astronomical measurements, but it is those measurements to which they must from time to time be adjusted. The day is the period of the earth's revolution on its axis; the (solar) year the time taken by the earth to travel in its orbit round the sun; the month, we have seen, is roughly related to the lunation, or the period of the moon's revolution about the earth.

For different chronological requirements the measurements are made in different ways. We need consider, however, only those which directly affect current calendars. The day with which we are concerned is the mean solar day, the *average* time, from midnight to midnight, which a point on a particular meridian on the earth's surface takes to return to the same point again with regard to the sun. (The difference between this solar day and the sidereal day—i.e., the day as measured by two consecutive transits of a star across the same meridian— amounts to about four minutes.) The meridian selected from which time for our purpose is counted is that which passes through Greenwich.

The month employed for calendrial reckoning is the synodic month, or lunation, which is 29 days 12 hours 44 minutes 2·8 seconds (29·530588 days or 4·2186 weeks). Twelve such lunations total 354 days 8 hours 48 minutes 34 seconds.

Our year is what is known as the tropical year. It is measured at the vernal equinox, the moment when the sun passes through the point of intersection of the celestial equator with the ecliptic, known as the First Point of Aries, to the same point again. Its length is 365·242199 days, or 365 days 5 hours 48 minutes 46 seconds.

3

When Pope Gregory carried out his very valuable reform of the Julian calendar in 1582 he adopted a compromise. Beneficial as was the reform it was still not complete and it did not render the calendar exact. It is slowly going wrong again—but very slowly. So far as the measurement of the years is concerned, it will be only one day out in 3,323 years, a matter which need not concern us in our everyday affairs, since that one-day adjustment will not fall due until the year 5,905, and can then be adjusted by dropping the nearest leap-year day.

What is now of more consequence is that the divisions of the single year were left precisely as they were in Roman days, with the sole exception of the dropping of a 29th of February three times in every four hundred years. January kept its 31 days, and February retained its 28, except for leap years, and March its 31 again. That left the first three months of the year with either 90 or 91 days according to whether it was a common or a leap year. April, May and June still held their 30, 31 and 30 days respectively, again making 91 days for the three months; while the remaining six months, running through the irregular numbers 31, 31, 30 and 31, 30, 31 and without any leap-year day to vary them, totalled 92 and 92 for each of these two quarters. So that the so-called 'half'-years could never be equal to each other. From January 1 to June 30 could be either 181 or 182 days in all, while the second 'half', from July 1 to December 31 must always total 184.

So far as we know, this matter was not even considered during the sixteenth and preceding centuries when the need for reform was under debate. It had no religious significance, and commerce had presumably not arrived at a position which called for semi-annual records. No special occasion marked the half-year, and there was no competitively-organised industry that demanded half-yearly or quarterly statistics.

For that matter no special event marks the passage of the half-year mark in our own time, nor does the quad-rennial leap-year day call forth any burst of enthusiasm to celebrate, however willing people may be, as many of us are, to find excuse for celebration. Which may be one of the good reasons, if not an important one, for switch-ing the leap year day to mid-year, as almost all calendar reformers propose. It would provide a neat dividing line, and an ideal moment for a break, or even a celebration.

How the months came to have their irregular sequence, their jumbled 31 and 30 and their odd 28–29, we shall see as we proceed. The unfortunate fact is that they have them. They date from the two Cæsars—Julius and Augustus; no change in their lengths has been made since. The fact that we have got along with them some-how for nearly two thousand years is nothing in favour. The operative word is 'somehow'. The cost in incon-venience, in strain on memory, in time lost in reference and computation has been and is incalculable, but cer-tainly great. All this has been apparent, even obvious, for at least a century, during the whole of which time it has been equally apparent that correction and consequent improvement could be quite a simple matter, affecting nobody injuriously and everybody beneficially. Still, it has not been done, although it has not been entirely for the want of trying.

On the whole, it can no doubt be accepted that the

calendar requires improvement, that its irregularities are defects, and this book takes that point of view. There are those, it is true, who hold that these very irregularities constitute an attraction. They are those who, understandably enough have a rooted aversion to discipline and regimentation. Irregular things they find more pleasing than regular. They prefer, they say, the inconsistencies and incalculability of the calendar as it is, rather than to know automatically that, for example, the 1st of June next or in 1999 will fall on a Friday.

One can understand and indeed sympathize with that point of view. Discipline, as we all know, can all too easily be carried too far. But there is also illogic, and illogicalities can also be carried too far. One cannot have irregularities or illogicality in a measuring instrument, and surely the calendar is just that—an instrument in daily use for measuring time. A measuring instrument, of all things, needs to be precision made—which is just what our present calendar is not.

Let us accept, then, that the irregularities of the calendar are defects, and let us attempt to set out those defects. They are by no means negligible. Listed, they are:

1. The months have four different lengths: 28, 29, 30 and 31 days;

2. Each year 'borrows' a day from the following year (two in leap years), so that no date falls on the same day of the week in two consecutive years;

3. A year, or a month, or a quarter can (and does) begin on any of the seven days of the week.

4. The four 'quarters' are not quarters at all; they consist of 90, 91, 92 and 92 days in ordinary years, and 91, 91, 92 and 92 days in leap years; nor are the half-years equal halves—in ordinary years they have 181 and 184 days respectively, and in leap years 182 and 184 days.

5. Because a month can begin on any day of the week and there are four kinds of month we have 28 different month-patterns.

6. There is no correspondence between dates and days from
    week to week, from month to month (with the single
    exception of February and March in non-leap years), or
    from year to year. To find the week-day of a date in the future
    requires complicated and disproportionate computation.
7. In all months each day of the week occurs a minimum of
    four times; in a month of 29 days one day of the week
    occurs five times (and it can be any of the seven days);
    in a month of 30 days, two days of the week occur five
    times; in a month of 31 days, three days occur five times.
    This erratic occurrence of the days of the week shifts from
    month to month.
8. The number of working days, i.e. week-days, varies with
    the months, from a minimum of 24 to a maximum of 27.

If this arraignment seems imposing, even damning,
when thus set out, and causes perhaps some little wonder
that nothing seems to have been done about it, that fact
arises possibly from the reason that we live only from day
to day. We manage with it, as we always have managed
with it, and we have, in fact, not having known any other,
become used to it. It is a case of (in the words of the old
music hall song) 'what you never have you never miss'.

It was not perhaps until what is vaguely known as the
Industrial Revolution set in that the calendar's shortcomings could have begun to obtrude on affairs outside
the religious sphere. The comparatively leisurely commerce and social amenities of the Middle Ages could
hardly have suffered much inconvenience from one
month containing more days than the next. Communications were slight and the science of comparative statistics
had not been born. There was little need for exactitude.

Today it is a different story. Social affairs and business
communications alike suffer from the haphazard arrangement of the present calendar. For making advance
arrangements, or, in the case of industry, for calculating
production or progress records, whether by months,
quarters or half-years, the calendar is about as inefficient

as any imposed system could be. There never has been called for a universal reform that could do so little harm and at the same time so much good, while in itself it would be so simple.

Here in the words of one supporter of such reform are some of the practical advantages which might result:

Government programmes, Acts of Parliament, and official records will be more easy to arrange and handle. P.A.Y.E. for example won't have to reckon with 53 weeks one year and 52 the next. Banks and financial institutions, at present working out interest rates and other calculations on the basis of varying months and quarters, will find it a godsend.

Likewise with industry and all large-scale concerns which, relying upon current statistics for their efficiency, have continually to make adjustments as (for example) between months with 24 week-days and those with 27.

Travel by air, land, sea or road will now be able to be scheduled without Sundays and holidays roaming all over the time-table. Landlords and tenants won't have to work out any more their fluctuating liabilities for quarterly and half-yearly rent periods. Law courts, schools, and academic institutions will be able to fix their 'terms' on regular days—instead of dealing in such cumbersome phrases as 'the first Tuesday after the first Monday in November'. In less advanced countries, the advantages will be even greater. . . .'[1]

Now, how is all this so highly desirable improvement to be brought about? Is it really so simple? That is what it is the purpose of this book to try to explain. But before we come to examine the calendar's shortcomings in detail and the innumerable propositions that have been put forward for their correction, it would be well to dwell for a while on the things that have gone before, and to relate something of the history of the calendar—of the various calendars.

It is a fascinating story, for it is a part of the story of the human race.

[1] James Avery Joyce, *Now is the Time.*

PART ONE

CHAPTER I

Before History

IT IS OFTEN said that the beginnings of the calendar are lost in antiquity, like the beginnings of history. The two are in fact lost together. They fade into each other in the dim past. The earliest traceable records of civilization are of no value until their date is established and unless they contain in themselves some such indication of their epoch.

History in its documentary sense can take us back no further than a few millenia, but there is pre-history. With the aid principally of archæology that science is carrying the record of human progress back into far greater distances. Occasionally it glimpses vestiges of the past that suggest civilizations of which no formal or documentary evidence survives.

No more interesting contribution to prehistory has been made than the calendar theory of the Tiahuanaco ruins. If the theory is correct, a monolithic gateway believed once to have formed an important part of a magnificent Temple to the Sun at Kalasasaya, high up in the Bolivian Cordilleras, has sculptured on its face a calendar which is not only the oldest in the world but itself takes us back into a culture which is far more ancient than anything historians have hitherto believed existed.

Tiahuanaco is a township on the border of the famous Lake Titicaca, 12,500 feet up in the Andes in Bolivia, and close to the border of Peru where once the Incas ruled. While the Inca civilization dated back only to about the tenth or eleventh century (A.D.) there preceded it in these mountain regions about Tiahuanaco

14

two culture periods which archæologists generally describe as Tiahuanaco I and Tiahuanaco II, going back to about the first century A.D. It was in 1943 that H. S. Bellamy[1] advanced the theory that the great Gateway of the Kalasasaya Sun Temple, usually attributed to one of the Tiahuanaco periods was really a relic of a culture infinitely older, that it dated from 'before the Flood', and that it actually carried its own message proving this.

The theory is startling. It postulates the existence of a moon before our present moon, circling the earth in the dimly distant past. Let it be said at once, however, that this theory is not conventionally accepted, although it is based on a cosmology evolved by the Viennese cosmolgist Hans Hoerdiger, whose theories are supported by 'Hoerdiger Societies' in various parts of the world.

The theory is, briefly, that sometime in the long past history of the earth, perhaps three hundred thousand years, there circled about our sphere a satellite, a moon, much smaller than our present moon, which, as it revolved, came slowly nearer and nearer to the earth. As over long periods of time it approached ever closer, it drew the seas and the oceans upwards towards it in a vast rising tide—a girdle-tide which practically encircled the earth about the equator, leaving the temperate zones dry and denuded to where the great ice-caps covered the polar extremes of the globe. Steadily it drove the men who peopled the earth higher and higher into the mountains.

Man, says Bellamy, was already well advanced in civilization, but this great girdle-tide, at least probably two or three miles high, came almost to wipe him out. In many places on the earth he was driven slowly up into the mountains, as in the Andes and in Tibet where he found a refuge, until at last this circling satellite disintegrated under its own gravitational and centrifugal forces and became a great comet of dust and meteors which were slowly dissipated on the earth itself.

[1] H. S. Bellamy, *Built Before the Flood* (Faber, 1943).

Then the great girdle-tide—the origin of all the primitive traditions concerned with the Flood—receded,
creating giant waves that surged back over the temperate
zones, in their turn drowning out all living beings
except perhaps a few refugee communities. Following
all this, the earth, through a long period of many
thousands of years had no moon to illumine the nights
until, somewhere about thirteen or fourteen thousand
B.C. it captured and held Luna, the wandering planet
that became our moon.

It is the calendar of one year in that distant period
of the pre-Moon Satellite, or what may perhaps be best
called the First Moon, that is given us on the Kalasasaya
Gateway at Tiahuanaco.

The historical and cultural implications of the theory
hardly fall within the province of this book, nor does
any debate on its astronomical tenability; it is too sharply
isolated from history and accepted pre-history in their
ordinary sense. However, whether the theory holds or
not, has substance or not, it does come within our pur-
view as illustrating the close connection of the calendar
with the earliest progress of man. The Calendar Gateway is undoubtedly a noble monument, and if Bellamy's
ingenious explanations of the symbolism of its interesting
sculpture are correct it tells of a time-system on the
earth which differed startlingly from present time division
in two respects.

The day was longer than our present day by several
hours; the month (the revolution of this moon around
the earth) was shorter than the day.

According to the theory, the Tiahuancan year was
divided into twelve parts, like our own, but it was purely
an arbitrary division, with no reference to months as we
understand them and such as have been responsible for
our own roughly four-week divisions. Perhaps this
early people had a duodecimal method of counting; it is
conceivable that twelve may have had a religious

significance. However that may be, that part of the
ornamentation of the Gateway which is assumed to be a
calendrical record is in the shape of an inverted T,
divided into twelve separate designs, the first a large
central 'capital' forming the upright of the T, and the
other eleven a horizontal meander of delightfully
stylized symbols, every single item and figure of which
has a meaning, it is said, recording the hours, the days,
and the lunations of passing time. Two of them in
particular are supposed to indicate the positions of the
solstices and the equinoxes.

Each of the sections is in the form of a square having a
central figure surrounded by a design of puma, condor or
toxodon heads and other traditional symbols. These
symbols are believed to signify the astronomical movements of the period. If they are correctly interpreted .
this First Moon was whizzing around the earth at a rate
of $447\frac{1}{4}$ times a year. This compares with the present
moon's between twelve and thirteen revolutions about
the earth per annum, and makes the Tiahuanacan
month, or, as it might more literally be described,
'moonth', less in length than the day.

The day, on the other hand, was longer than at
present, the earth turning on its axis not 365 and a
fraction times a year as now, but only 298 and a fraction,
which gave the day a length of rather more than 29
hours. This was partly due to the 'braking' action of the
great tidal concentration of the water—the girdle tide
about the equator.

Two curious winged figures found on each of the
squares which represent the periods of time most nearly
equivalent to what would be our months of March and
September are interpreted to mark the occurrence of
the equinoxes, while two other designs placed centrally
between them in 'March' and 'September' indicate the
solstices. Since the occurrence of these phenomena has
nothing to do with the moon, in any case, it is held that

their appearance on the Tiahuanacan 'calendar' in no
way belittles the general theory, but tends on the contrary to support it, since they are in exact agreement
with modern astronomical observation. It is not suggested that the earth's orbit in relation to the sun has
varied: the year three thousand centuries ago was much
the same as now. Only the variation in the speed of the
earth on its axis, and the theory of the existence of a
prior moon which is alleged to have disintegrated and
made way for our own moon arise out of this startling
interpretation of the message of the Calendar Gateway
of Tiahuanaco.

But if the interpretation is right, or even approximately right, it serves to show the outstanding place the
calendar has held in the history of mankind. It shows that
there were calendars 'before the Flood'.

CHAPTER II

The Beginnings

THE MOST ANCIENT calendar relic we have in Britain is Stonehenge. It is a survival not only of the religion of the ancient Britons but of their astronomical erudition. Its alignment bears witness to an exact knowledge of the annual occurrence of the summer solstice, and the calculation of the midsummer day on which the sun would rise at its most north-easterly point and mark off another year. Other megolithic relics are scattered about southern Britain and northern France all of which reflect the concern of their builders—presumably the priests—with the celestial cycle of events. In Egypt the angular alignment of the great pyramids carries the same message.

Astronomy is probably the oldest of the sciences. On it the most primitive agriculture depended. Homo sapiens must very early have connected the sowing and reaping of the land, and the repetitive fertility of animal life with the phenomena of the sky and the seasons, with the sun, and most importantly with the moon.

The moon is an automatic calendar. One imagines that the earliest intelligence could cope with it for the count of the passage of time. The next moon, or two moons ago, must have been within the compass even of those whose arithmetic was limited to 'one, two, plenty'. Such consciousness might be older than language.

But the moon does not fit in with the seasons, or the

sun. Yet night and day, or darkness and light, were connected obviously with both. None of these things
exactly fitted the others. Calendar history is the story of
man's (always more or less vain) efforts to make them
agree, or to keep track of them all in some inclusive
system. The day of course agreed with the sun, and to
some extent the moon, but the moon was sometimes
visible in the daytime, though the sun never at night,
and the winter or the summer depended on whether the
sun was low or high in the sky at mid-day. Darkness, the
moon, the weather; the day, the month, the cycle of
seasons, the sun; the gradually changing stars. These
were the incommensurables. One can only imagine the
slow dawning of consciousness of all these factors
in time. The first counting instrument was probably
the notched stick, or the scratched stone, and by this
means some measure of time could be kept. Dealing
with days in this way would have been simple, with
moons not much more difficult, but with the seasons
it was a different matter: the intervals were long and the
sky a vast area.

After the notched stick there probably came the
gnomon, a device for measuring shadows. In its simplest
form it was merely a stick stuck into the ground. Later
it became the sundial. Mid-day was when the shadow
thrown by the stick was shortest on any particular day;
midsummer when it was at its very shortest. Such
moments could early have had their significance. The
combination of the two ideas, the gnomon and the
notches, or scratches on a cave wall, made a calendar, of
sorts. Marked sticks, providing records thus obtained,
have survived. The high noon of the short shadow could
have competed with the sunrise as the beginning of a
new day, as sunset has frequently done, and moon-rise,
as in the Moslem calendar today, and even moon-set.
Came in time the clepsydra, or water clock, for dividing
the day into measured parts and the primitive candle,

that would mark off the passing hours by the time of its burning, and, ultimately, clocks.

It is obviously impossible to say when and how the counting of time began. Various civilizations have selected various beginnings for their respective eras. The Jewish religious calendar computes time from the supposed date of the creation, which is the longest continuous reckoning; an Indian historical era takes the count back to 3102 B.C. while Chinese chronology traditionally begins in 2397 B.C. According to eminent and highly-reputed scholars, the Egyptians were using a calendar as long ago as 4236[1] or 4241[2] B.C., which predates the Jewish calendar by several hundred years.

The Egyptian story of calendar development seems to be the clearest. It is believed, and it seems only reasonable to accept that the earliest calendars of all communities were based on lunar observation, and that the approximation of twelve provided the foundation of the year.

The Egyptians used the symbol of the crescent moon to mean a month long after they are known to have abandoned the lunar for the solar year, and to have been employing a calendar of 12 months of 30 days and 5 additional days to make up the 365-day solar year.

The key to the conception of this solar year lies in the fact that the Egyptian communities were centred about the great River Nile, whose annual flooding has for thousands of years been the most important feature of Egyptian civilization and culture. Between successive risings of the water the Egyptians designated three seasons: the season of the inundations, the season of the sowing, and the season of the harvest. This repetitive natural happening came to be associated with the heliacal rising of the 'dog star' Sirius, the brightest star they saw in the heavens.

[1] James Henry Breasted, *Ancient Times*, quoted by Dr. B. D. Panth.
[2] S. H. Hooke, *New Year's Day* (1927).

In the course of time, it must have been noted that the rising of the star was moving slowly through the seasons, one day in every four years, so that over a cycle of 1,461 years the first of the month of Thoth, the New Year of the Egyptians, had drifted over the entire calendar from one extreme to the other, and occupied every one of the 365 day-and-night days of the calendar year. 'In these 1,461 years the star Sirius and the River Nile rose only 1,460 times. This made the astonomers realize that 1,461 years of 365 days were equal to 1,460 years of 365¼ days. It was through this queer discrepancy that the Egyptian astronomers recognized the length of the solar year to be 365¼ days'.[1]

Then followed the first battle for the reform of a calendar of which we have any knowledge. 'The astronomers attempted to introduce necessary reforms to bring the calendar up to date. But the authoritarian priests were powerfully established and, considering the calendar as their peculiarly private preserve, resented any trespass. The struggle for change continued for centuries, until finally, in 238 B.C., by the Decree of Canopus, of King Ptolemy III, Euergetes, the erratic quality of the calendar was eliminated. The decree provided for the intercalation of a day at the end of every four years. This intercalation resulted in a leap year of 366 days, and so the year came to be recognized as averaging 365·25 days. The calendar then assumed a decidedly more accurate and stable form, and marked the beginning of our present solar calendar'.

The famous Canopus Stone was discovered in 1886. Translated by E. A. Wallis Budge, keeper of the Egyptian and Assyrian Antiquities in the British Museum, it throws much light on early calendar story. It reads:

> In order that it may happen that that which hath been decreed to be done at each season of the year may be done in accordance with the position which the heavens have with

[1] B. D. Panth, *Consider the Calendar* (Columbia University, 1944).

reference to the things which have to be performed at the
present time, so that occasion may not be given, and the case
may not arise, that some of the festivals which are celebrated
in Egypt in the winter should come to be observed in the
summer, in consequence of the rising of Sirius advancing one
day every four years, and on the other hand, some of the festivals which are at the present time celebrated in the winter, a
thing which actually happened in the times which are past,
and would happen at the present time if the year consisted of
360 and the five days which have been observed: from this time
onwards one day, as festival of the Good-doing Gods, shall be
added every four years to the five additional days which come
before the New Year, so that it may happen that every man
shall know that the small amount (of time) which was lacking
in the arrangement of the seasons and of the year, and in the
things which passed as laws (or, principles) for the knowledge
of their movements, hath been corrected, and that it hath been
supplied by the Good-doing Gods.[1]

Thus in one part of the world the solar calendar had
reached, two thousand years ago, as high a degree of
exactitude as it was to attain, with one short exception,
until the sixteenth century A.D. and the Gregorian
reform of the Julian calendar which then took place. The
leap year idea, however, does not appear to have been an
unqualified success even in Egypt, for the same authority
states that 'how long the reform was carried out at Canopus
cannot be said, but it certainly does not appear to have been
adopted generally'. Vested interests were already powerful.
While this calendrical evolution was taking its slow
course in Egypt, other civilizations and cultures about
the Mediterranean and in the great Mesopotamian plain,
were evolving their own chronological processes.
Over the last few decades archeological exploration
and research on the sites of the ancient Babylonian and
Assyrian civilizations has thrown much light on the

[1] F. A. Wallis Budge, *The Decree of Canopus* (Kegan Paul, London,
1904).

achievements and customs of the peoples which flourished so mightily in the lost world between and about the Tigris and the Euphrates. But the picture of the calendars they used is still not so clear as that of the Egyptians. The Sumerians and Chaldeans, of old Babylonia, appear to have had a time system based on the lunar month, with additional months intercalated to keep time in step with the seasons.

This seems to have gone on for some thousands of years, but without any regular system to govern the intercalation of the extra months 'until the Chaldean astronomer Kidinnu (or Cidenas) introduced the 19-year cycle in 382 B.C. The Chaldeans were the priestly caste of Babylon, by whom astrology was brought to a well-developed system. They kept careful records of their astronomical observations and, though they knew that the length of the tropical year was $365\frac{1}{4}$ days, they used the fixed year of 365 days for the recording of their observations and for facilitating their calculations. It is not known whether this fixed year was taken over from the Egyptians or found independently. It appears to have been used in Babylon from the time of Nabonassar. Various astronomical periods were determined by the Chaldeans with amazing accuracy'.[1]

In ancient Greece a parallel development was taking place. There also in the first millenium B.C. astronomy made amazing progress, and they had a luni-solar calendar from a very early date. 'According to Macrobius the normal Greek year was a lunar twelve-month of 354 days. Knowing that the solar year comprises $365\frac{1}{4}$ days they added $11\frac{1}{4} \times 8$, making 90 days every eight years. This intercalation was divided into three embolismic (extra) months of 30 days. The eight-year cycle was known as the Octæteris'.[2]

[1] Sir H. Spencer Jones, *The Calendar: Past, Present and Future.*

[2] Alexander Philip, *The Calendar* (Cambridge University Press, 1921).

This adding of three artificial months every eight years to the years based on 12 lunar months was possibly the first methodical cycle introduced into the calendar in the universal effort to adjust lunar months to solar years—the perpetual problem which has lasted into the present time. This early Greek method, credited to Cleostratos, an Ionian astronomer who also introduced the signs of the Zodiac, was not however, exact; but a later Athenian astronomer, Meton, in 432 B.C. devised a 19-year cycle which not only fulfilled this purpose for the early Greeks, but has lasted to the present time as a factor in the calculation of the Christian Easter. The 19-year cycle is also an essential feature of the Jewish calendar. It requires that seven times in every nineteen years the year should consist of thirteen (lunar) months, of 29 or 30 days.

The astonishing advance of the Greeks in astronomy is well indicated by the fact that in the second century B.C. Hipparchos of Nicæa, who, using older Greek and Chaldean observations, discovered the precession of the equinoxes and distinguished between the sidereal and tropical year, estimated the latter to be 365 days 5 hours 55 minutes and 12 seconds, which was only 6 minutes and 26 seconds out of its true length.[1] This is a remarkable fact which has a tremendous bearing on our present calendar, for it shows that the true length of the year was more nearly known in Julius Cæsar's time than is generally supposed.

The Roman calendar has its own development but, since it was to lead in a straight line to our own, we will first glance at what was going on across the other side of the world. The calendars of the Far East developed along their own individual lines and independently of those in the countries around the Mediterranean or what we now conveniently call the Middle East. Yet there would

[1] G. Sarton, *Introduction to the History of Science* (Carnegie Institute, Washington).

c

seem to be a link which postulates one of history's intriguing mysteries. This is concerned with the origin of a feature of the ancient Chinese calendars known as the cycle of the twelve animals.

In his classic *Introduction to the History of Science* Professor Sarton writes:

> In every Eastern country, from Turkestan to Japan, they use a cycle of twelve animals, corresponding to twelve consecutive years. The animals are always placed in the same order:
>
> mouse or rat, ox, tiger or panther;
> hare, dragon or crocodile, snake;
> horse, sheep or goat, monkey;
> chicken, dog, pig or boar.
>
> The same animals are used also to designate twelve successive months, twelve days, or twelve double hours—just as in the Greco-roman world successive hours, days, months, years and epochs were placed under the domination of the seven planets and designated by them. According to F. Boll, this cycle of twelve animals originated in Egypt in the first century. If this is correct, it gives one proof of the immense influence exerted by the Hellenistic upon the Asian and Chinese civilizations.

Discussion of this influence and the routes by which it may have reached the Celestial Kingdom at such a period is outside the scope of our study but it illustrates the importance of the calendar in the history of earliest times. The Chinese calendar goes back much earlier than the first century, for there is a record of its being 're-formed' in the year 104 B.C. by the astronomer Lo Hsia Hung, who flourished under the Western Han about the time of Hipparchos, the Greek astronomer to whom is credited the discovery of the precession of the equinoxes. This knowledge, however, had not travelled so far in the next 120 years, for sometime between 7 B.C. and 22 A.D. a treatise on the calendar was written by Lin Hsin, the imperial librarian, of whom Sarton reports: 'He did not know of the precession of the equinoxes and to reconcile the tropical and sidereal years he introduced an enormous period, like the Hindu Kalpa, a period of 23,639,040 years. He determined in the most artificial manner the chronology of prehistoric China'. There were reforms of the calendar again in 123 and in 385, and further corrections and elaborations in 566 and 1065, by which time the picturesque system had been evolved which was to last into the twentieth century.

In Japan the story of the earliest calendars is again not so clear. Time reckoning was based on the regular sequence of the seasons and the phases of the moon, and 'some scholar of the time was commissioned to publish in advance a calendar (*hi-oki*) which was no doubt very summary.[1] But in the seventh century the Japanese adopted the Chinese calendar of the period and continued to follow the Chinese system until 1872.

The principle of this was the sexagesimal cycle, which was brought to its perfection in Japan by the Japanese astronomer Abe Seimei, who flourished under Murakami-tenno in the tenth century. The cycle itself, called *Chia-tzu*, says Sarton, is immemorial. The Chinese themselves ascribe it to the Yellow Emperor, Huang Ti, one of their legendary rulers (2698 to 2598 B.C.) but there is no evidence of it before the Han dynasty. It is a period of 60 years, 'a cycle of Cathay', each year having the name of two characters. One of these is taken from the ten (or Heaven) stems, i.e. the five elements, each counted twice, and the other from the series of twelve (or Earth) twigs (*ti-chih*), each of which has an animal name. This is the cycle of the twelve animals.

'In the year 522 the King of Kudara (Korea) sent some astronomers to Japan, who drew up a calendar which was not accepted, but in 602, the Buddhist *bonze*, Kwanroka, also from Kudara, is said to have brought with him to Japan the books used in China to make a calendar. "This time a Japanese, Yakoshiso Tamafuru,

[1] E. Papinot, *Historical Dictionary of Japan* (Shanghai, 1920).

was appointed to study the new science, and from the first day of the new year 604, the Chinese calendar was adopted. It was called Genko-reki". There were Jananese modifications and elaborations in 673, 856 and 861, but then it reached its final form, and continued in use in the country for 823 years'.

The following is an outline of how this interesting calendar worked:

The five stems or trunks (*jikkau*, in Japanese) were formed of the five elements: wood (*ki*), fire (*hi*), earth (*tsuchi*), metal (*ka*), and water (*mizu*). Each of these is counted twice, once as a 'senior brother' (*e*) and then as a 'junior brother' (*to*), thus:

Ki-ni-e	..	Elder brother of the wood
ki-no-to	..	Younger brother of the wood
Hi-no-e	..	Elder brother of the fire
hi-no-to	..	Younger brother of the fire
Tsuchi-no-e	..	Elder brother of the earth
tsuchi-no-to	..	Younger brother of the earth
Ka-no-e	..	Elder brother of the metal
ka-no-to	..	Younger brother of the metal
Mizi-no-e	..	Elder brother of the water
Mizi-no-to	..	Younger brother of the water

These were then combined with the twelve 'twigs':

1. *Ne*	Rat	5. *Tatsu*	Dragon	9. *Saru*	Monkey
2. *Ushi*	Ox	6. *Mi*	Serpent	10. *Tori*	Cock
3. *Toro*	Tiger	7. *Uma*	Horse	11. *Inu*	Dog
4. *U*	Hare	8. *Hitsuji*	Goat	12. *I*	Boar

The sequence of years therefore works out like the following, which is the calendar for the first years of the present century:

1900	*Ka-no-e*	*Ne*	..	Year of the Rat
1	*Ka-no-to*	*Ushi*	..	Year of the Ox
2	*Mizi-no-e*	*Toro*	..	Year of the Tiger
3	*Mizi-no-to*	*U*	..	Year of the Hare

4	*Ki-no-e*	Tatsu	..	Year of the Dragon
5	*Ki-no-to*	Mi	..	Year of the Serpent
6	*Hi-no-e*	Uma	..	Year of the Horse
7	*Hi-no-to*	Hitsuji	..	Year of the Goat
8	*Tsuchi-no-e*	Saru	..	Year of the Monkey
9	*Tsuchi-no-to*	Tori	..	Year of the Cock
10	*Ka-no-e*	Inu	..	Year of the Dog
11	*Ka-no-to*	I	..	Year of the Boar
12	*Mixi-no-e*	Ne	..	Year of the Rat
13	*Mizi-no-to*	Ushi	..	Year of the Ox
14	*Ki-no-e*	Toro	..	Year of the Tiger
15	*Ki-no-to*	U	..	Year of the Hare
16	*Hi-no-e*	Tatsu	..	Year of the Dragon
17	*Hi-no-to*	Mi	..	Year of the Serpent
18	*Tsuchi-no-e*	Uma	..	Year of the Horse
19	*Tsuchi-no-to*	Hitsuji	..	Year of the Goat
1920	*Ka-no-e*	Saru	..	Year of the Monkey

The divisions of the year into seasons, months and days are equally picturesque, but in 1873 for official purposes the Japanese adopted the Gregorian calendar. China did the same in 1912.

CHAPTER III

In Ancient Mexico

ARCHÆOLOGY AND documentary research have produced no more interesting historical material, so far as the calendar is concerned, than that relating to the calendars of central and northern South America—the strange calendars of the Mayas, the Incas and the Aztecs. At the beginning of this book we have touched on the amazing theory of Mr. H. S. Bellamy as to the famous Tiahuanaco ruins in Bolivia and the celebrated Calendar Gate. If there is anything in the theory, that relic takes us back not merely thousands of years into calendar history, but tens and perhaps hundreds of thousands.

However, it finds little acceptance outside of the Hoerbiger Society and the Bellamy school (although the writer for one feels no inclination to eschew or pooh-pooh it) and it will probably remain long a subject of controversy. Not so the calendrical lore of the Central American races of the millenium or so before the Spanish Conquest. Of that a great deal is now known, and the pattern of their calendars is clear, if strange.

Of these races, the Aztecs had devised the most perfect, if also the most complex time system: it is so complex that for a long time its details defeated the scholars and historians. Up to 1892, for example, the question of a key to the calendar system was still being discussed, as is shown in the following paragraph from an English scientific journal of that year:[1]

[1] *Nature*, December 15, 1892.

At the recent meeting of the Congress of Americanists at
Huelva, Mrs. Zeila Nuttall, of the Peabody Museum of
American Archæology and Ethnology, presented a preliminary
note on the calendar system of the ancient Aztecs. Guided by a
statement in Hispano-Mexican MS. which she has recently
discovered in the National Central Library of Florence, Mrs.
Nuttall claims to have found the key to the Aztec calendar
system.

She exhibited tables showing that the Mexican cycle was
13,515 days, and that it comprised 52 ritual years (less five
days at the end of the cycle) of 260 days each, or 51 lunar
years of 265 days each, based on nine moons, or 37 solar years
of 365 days each. At the end of the 51st lunar year ten intercalary days placed the solar years in agreement with the lunar
years in such a manner that the new cycle recommenced in the
same solar and lunar positions as the 13,515 preceding days.
Each period commenced with a day bearing one of four names:
Acatl, Tecpatl, Calli, or Tochtali.

The journal added that 'the calendar system and tables,
fourteen metres long, were subsequently placed on
exhibition in the Spanish Historical Exhibition at
Madrid.'

That was revealing, but it had missed an essential
point about the Aztec calendar—the fundamental importance to the race of the number 13. However, a couple
of years later, the same authority returned to the subject
in reporting a lecture given by Dr. D. G. Brinton of the
American Philosophical Society.[1] 'The native races of
Mexico and Central America', said *Nature*, 'used a
calendar differing completely from those employed by
the ancient nations of the Old World to reckon time.
Many explanations of the origin of the calendar have
been suggested, some referring it to series of recurring
events in nature, others to astronomical phenomena,
while a third section of inquirers regard it as purely
mythical and terrestrial'.

[1] *Nature*, June 28, 1894.

Dr. Brinton had sought the solution from the point of view of linguistics and symbolism. He explained that the basis of the system was a 'month' of 20 days. Each day was named after some object, animate or inanimate, and each day also had a number. These numbers, however, did not run from 1 to 20, but only from 1 to 13, when the numbering started again. Thus the same name and number for any one day would not occur a second time until after 260 (20 × 13) days had elapsed. So a 260-day cycle was created, which made the Aztec 'year'.

Dr. Brinton's linguistic analysis of names of the 20 days in various dialects and languages showed that they were all identical in meaning, and therefore must have had the same origin. By arranging the symbols representing the day names in the order 1 to 20, it was found that they exhibited a sequence covering the career of human life, from birth until death at an old age. Thus, in the five languages examined, the name of the first day signified beginning, that of the tenth day, success (through hardship and suffering); of the eleventh difficulties surmounted; of the thirteenth advancing years; of the eighteenth war and death; of the twentieth, the sun or 'house of the soul'.

It appears therefore that the calendar conveyed a philosophical conception of life; the number 20 is believed to have originated from the vigesimal system of counting, arising from finger-and-toe calculation, and it is significant that the number also signified 'completed' or 'filled up'. In this way, apparently, the number of days came to represent symbolically 'the whole of man, his complete nature and destiny, and mystically to shadow forth and embody all the unseen potencies which make or mar his fortunes all his life'.

As for the 13 names, or varieties of names, which were applied to each day of the same number during the year, 'apparently the ancient seers of Mexico and Central America believed that by assigning 13 modes of

activity to each of the 20 headings under which the
agencies that influence human life were arranged, they
had taken into account the 13 possible relations of each
to both the material and immaterial worlds: and the
fact that the result of 20 × 13 is 260 days, or approximately nine months, that is, the period from conception
to birth, would, according to Dr. Brinton, have appeared
to confirm the mystic potensies of these cardinal
numbers'.

But this 260-day sequence, or *Tonalpolhualli*, interesting as it is, did not complete the Aztec calendar
system. There was also used, in conjunction with it, a
solar calendar of 360 days, which was made up of 18
months each of 20 days and rounded off with five
'unlucky' days to complete the solar year. Later researches have done much to explain the complex inter-
weaving of these calendars and their significance in the
Aztec religion. The 260-day calendar was in fact essentially religious, and every day had its appointed ritual.
The keeping of the calendar and the 'complicated
astronomic and mathematical computations that kept the
solar and religious calendars in harmony with the passage
of the seasons was the province of the priesthood'.[1]

Dr. Vaillant describes the Aztec system as completely
theocratic. 'The gods ruled: the priests interpreted and
interposed; and the people obeyed, not the priests, but
the rhythm of action whereby the gods lived'. This
rhythm was the calendar. A combination of the two
systems permitted the numbering of years, which were
counted not on an infinite scale, as with us, but in terms
of a 52-year cycle. A god or goddess presided over each
of the list of 20 days and of each of the 20 periods of
'weeks' of 13 days. 'The gods of the weeks', says Vaillant,
followed the same order as the day gods, with the
exception that the god of the eleventh day was dropped
from the list, moving the remainder in order up one

[1] G. C. Vaillant, *The Aztecs of Mexico* (Pelican Books).

place each. The resulting vacancy in the twentieth week
was filled by two divinities who exercised joint control. ...
Finally, 13 of these gods influenced the 13 stations of the
Aztec day and 9 held sway over the night hours'. The
lists of gods—of months, weeks, days and nights, connected with the calendar, is of course imposing, but,
argues this writer, 'it is improbable that the ordinary
communicant daily honoured each god any more than a
Catholic layman prays daily to each saint in the calendar.
He did reverence in terms of his own spiritual and actual
necessity'. However, the deplorable human sacrifices
that were so large a part of the Aztec calendrical ritual
takes it as far away from the Christian calendar as does
its peculiar numeration.

The 52-year period was observed also by the Mayans,
who, according to some authorities, began counting the
days as far back as August 6 613 B.C. although the
earliest date yet found in their inscriptions and de-
ciphered is 98 B.C.[1]

'Some of the pyramids in the centre of the country',
writes N. P. Wright in *Mexican Kaleidoscope* show in
their construction a relationship to the time calculations
of their builders, in that their outermost walls concealed
smaller, earlier pyramids. In the case of the pyramid at
Penayuca, for example, it has been possible to lay open
several such constructions one within the other, and it is
accepted that each was built above and around the last
at periods of 52 years, each new construction coinciding
with the great feasts held at the end of each 52-year
cycle. And as different ceramic types and other objects
were encountered within each period, it was a simple
matter to date them to the nearest 52 years'.

Referring to the interesting stelæ—those inscribed
upright calendar stones—which archæologists have
found in various parts of Mexico and Central America,
Mr. Wright states:

[1] Norman Pelham Wright *Mexican Kaleidoscope* (Heineman 1947).

Almost the sole object of erecting these stelæ was to com-
memorate dates—not historical dates, be it mentioned, but
purely ceremonial dates marking calendar periods. This flair
for time-calculation appears to have been merely a means to
an end, for the elaborate Mayan calendar really served as an
aid to agriculture.

It seems as though these people were very conscious of the
fact that they were the first people to benefit from maize
cultivation. It seems as though they were fanatically determined to prosecute agriculture with the maximum efficiency
with the aid of a realistic, scientific and workable calendrical
system. Their efforts in the latter direction led them on to
astronomy and abstractions, for which they now had time to
spare as maize had obviated the necessity for hunting and
eased the struggle for existence. The stelæ themselves are impressive and graceful, and many are in an excellent state of
preservation. Most are adorned on one or two sides with
colossal human figures in priestly vestments or those of gods,
the remaining sides being as a rule covered with the hiero-
glyphic inscriptions.

Strangely enough the Incas, whose civilization in
many ways was even more advanced than that of the
Aztecs, had not developed a calendrical system of anything like the same nature. According to W. H. Prescott,
whose monumental *History of the Conquest of Peru*[1] is
still the most interesting authority, they divided their
year into twelve lunar months, each of which was distinguished by an appropriate festival. They also had
weeks, though of what length, whether of seven, nine
or ten days, is uncertain.

Their lunar calendar appears to have been corrected
from time to time by the use of the gnomon. 'As their
lunar year would necessarily fall short of the true time,
they rectified their calendar by solar observations by
means of a number of cylindrical columns raised on the

[1] W. H. Prescott, *History of the Conquest of Peru* (Geo. Allen and
Unwin, 1935 Edition).

high lands round Cuzco, which served them for taking azimuths; and by measuring these shadows they ascertained the exact times of the solstices. The period of the equinoxes they determined by the help of a solitary pillar, or gnomon, placed in the centre of a circle, which was described in the area of the great temple and traversed by a diameter that was drawn from east to west. When the shadows were scarcely visible under the noontide rays of the sun, they said that "the god sat with all his light upon the column" '.

CHAPTER IV

From Julius to Gregory

THE JULIAN CALENDAR—named after Julius Cæsar —was the direct parent of the Gregorian calendar, which almost all the world uses to-day. Rome had calendars before the Julian, but it was Cæsar who took the decisive step of abolishing the unsatisfactory time system current in the Roman empire when he took over, and making a completely fresh start. Only in a powerful and wide-spread community of nations such as the Roman could it have been done with such remarkable success, and perhaps equally only an individual as forceful as Cæsar could have done it. It was an act as far-reaching in its effects as any in the frame of Roman progress, for it smoothed out and unified the imperial communications.

Latin authors differ as to the earliest calendar in use. At the date accepted as the foundation year of Rome— 753 B.C.—the so-called year may have contained only ten months, totalling 304 days. Alexander Philip, quoting Macrobius and Censorius, gave the months April, June, Sexilis, September, November and December having each 30 days, and March, May, Quintilis and October, each with 31. Total, 304. The ten months are confirmed by Ovid, but Philip quotes also other authors who dispute the point. An interesting theory put forward elsewhere is that the primitive inhabitants of the northern territory recognized as worth counting only the days of these ten months: that throughout the remaining 50 or 60 days through the depth of winter when storms raged and life was practically frozen and impossible, they hibernated like bears in their caves, and the time was not worth counting. . . .

A little difficult to accept, but a theory. In any case the calendar began to take shape in the time of Numa Pompilius, second Roman king who, however, according to one authority[1] 'belongs to legend and not to history' but whose 'reign is supposed to have lasted from 715 to 673 B.C.' Whether he existed or not, he is credited with inserting January and February into the calendar, and rounding it off to the proper number of days, which was 354, so that obviously it was the usual original lunar calendar of the ancients everywhere. The names of the months, with two exceptions, were those we use to-day, but the year began with March. To keep his lunar years synchronized with the seasons, Numa is believed to have added or intercalated an additional month from time to time: the month of Mercedonius.

Some minor revisions were made by the Decemvirs, the supreme body of magistrates, in the fifth century B.C., but because of this lack of equation between the lunar and solar years and the necessity of intercalation the calendar became in time an extremely unreliable instrument, though only through mishandling. This mishandling was the work of the pontiffs, 'the chief sacred college of Rome . . . which possessed considerable political power through its control of the calendar and its power to intercalate days and regulate festivals'. From Censorius we learn;[2] 'The Pontiffs were charged with making the intercalation, but most of them, on account of enmity or friendship, shortened or lengthened the term of a magistrate, and intercalcating more or less according to their pleasure, caused a farmer of the revenue to gain or lose according to the length of the

[1] *Everyman's Encyclopedia.* Article on Numa.
[2] E. Achelis, *The Calendar for Everybody*, quoting *Popular Astronomy* (U.S.A., November 1919).

year, thus making worse what was given to them to correct'.

It was Julius Cæsar who came to the rescue. When he assumed power (and incidentally became Pontifex Maximus, head of the sacred college) the calendar was badly out of gear. The vernal equinox which should have been related to the start of the year, was occurring more than two months out of place, and religious festivals had meandered considerably away from their appropriate positions in the seasons.

He decided, it would seem, to do the thing thoroughly. For this purpose, he called to Rome the Greek astronomer Sosigenes, then carrying on his calling in Alexandria. Not much is known about Sosigenes beyond these bare facts of his nationality and location, but it has a significant bearing on Cæsar's wisdom that he should have been selected as scientific adviser, for it was in Greece and Egypt that astronomy had reached its highest degree of development. Sosigenes might be assumed to have been familiar with the latest advances in both countries.

The Julian calendar which resulted was undoubtedly a brilliant piece of work. It was the first true 'perpetual' calendar, that is, a calendar which began on the same day each new year, as contrasted with lunar systems, or intercalary calendars where the year's beginning varies. Its greatest achievement, however, was the definite institution of the quadrennial leap year which had been attempted in Egypt but had failed there to be accepted. Sosigenes took the Egyptian measure of the year as $365\frac{1}{4}$ days, and Cæsar repeated the Ptolemaic edict that an extra day should be counted in every fourth year, which was calculated to keep the new calendar synchronized with the seasons in four-year cycles. The lengths of the twelve months (Mercedonius, the occasional thirteenth, being completely eliminated) were adjusted to total 365 in ordinary years, and one of the

THE ROMAN CALENDAR

CALENDARIUM

Our days of the Month	March, May, July, October, have 31 days	January, August, December, have 31 days	April, June, September, November, have 30 days	February has 28 days and in Leap Year 29
1	KALENDIS*	KALENDIS	KALENDIS	KALENDIS
2	VI ⎤	IV ⎤ ante	IV ⎤ ante	IV ⎤ ante
3	V ⎬ ante	III ⎭ Nonas	III ⎭ Nonas	III ⎭ Nonas
4	IV ⎥ Nonas	Pridie Nonas	Pridie Nonas	Pridie Nonas
5	III ⎦	NONIS	NONIS	NONIS
6	Pridie Nonas	VIII ⎤	VIII ⎤	VIII
7	NONIS	VII ⎥	VII ⎥	VII
8	VIII ⎤	VI ⎬ ante	VI ⎬ ante	VI
9	VII ⎥	V ⎭ Idus	V ⎭ Idus	V
10	VI ⎬ ante	IV ⎥	IV ⎥	IV
11	V ⎭ Idus	III ⎦	III ⎦	III
12	IV ⎥	Pridie Idus	Pridie Idus	Pridie Idus
13	III ⎦	IDIBUS	IDIBUS	IDIBUS
14	Pridie Idus	XIX ⎤	XVIII ⎤	XVI
15	IDIBUS	XVIII	XVII	XV
16	XVII	XVII	XVI	XIV
17	XVI	XVI	XV	XIII
18	XV	XV	XIV	XII
19	XIV	XIV	XIII	XI
20	XIII	XIII	XII	X
21	XII	XII	XI	IX
22	XI	XI	X	VIII
23	X	X	IX	VII
24	IX	IX	VIII	VI
25	VIII	VIII	VII	V
26	VII	VII	VI	IV
27	VI	VI	V	III
28	V	V	IV	Pridie Kalendas Martias
29	IV	IV	III	In Leap-Year,
30	III	III	Pride Kalendas	Feb. 24 (a. d.
31	Pridie Kalendas (Apriles, Junias, Sextiles, Novembres).	Pridie Kalendas (Februarias, Septembres, Januarias).	(Maias, Quiriles, Octobres, Decembres).	vi. Kal. Mart.) was reckoned twice. Hence this day was called bis-sextus, and the year annus bissextus.

The 2nd–31st entries for the first three month columns are braced as: Ante Kalendas (of the month following). The February column entries 14–27 are braced as: Ante Kalendas Martias.

*The words are given in the Albative Case, the form employed in assigning a date.

days of February was to be duplicated when leap year came round, to make the 366.

It seemed simple, and perfect, and indeed it was almost so, but in fact the $365\frac{1}{4}$ figure as the measure of the number of days in the years was not quite exact. We have seen that a closer estimate had been made in Greece, and it is hard to believe that Sosigenes would not have known of it, and have been capable of working out a cycle that would have made allowances for the slight difference; on the other hand, one may assume that if Cæsar was advised of the discrepancy he was also informed that it would not amount to more than a day in a very long time—a matter of more than two centuries according to the Hipparchus reckoning—and that he justifiably regarded it as negligible.

As it was, the innovation was complicated enough. To adjust the new calendar to the old and to get a correct start, the old year had to be extended to the unprecedented and artificial length of 445 days. That was the year 708 A.U.C. (*Ab Urbe Condita*, in Roman delineation) or 46 B.C. (in the later Christian description). It became known as the 'year of confusion'.

A peculiar feature of the Julian calendar was its method of enumerating the days. The months were each divided into three parts: the Kalends, the Nones, and the Ides, and the days counted *backwards*. The day before the Kalend, or the None, or the Ide of a month was called *Pridie*, and the day before that the 3rd of that period, and the day before that again the 4th, and so on. Even the leap-years did not disturb the sequence, for when February had an extra day, that day, which was observed as the 6th before the March Kalend, was simply repeated, there being two '6ths', a fact which is commemorated in the word 'bisextile', meaning double sixth, the official term for describing our own leap year, in spite of our having moved the leap year day to the end of the month of February. The Roman 6th (counting

D

backwards from the March Kalend) would have coincided with our February 24.

The table of months and days of the Roman calendar on page 40 shows how easy it is to count the days backwards—after a little study. The Romans had of course to remember the lengths of their months to get their dates right, but so have we. The preponderance of 31-day months was largely due originally to the superstitious Roman dislike of even numbers. It was the grafting of the week on to the Julian calendar that was responsible for its loss of 'perpetualness'[1] and consequently for its major inconvenience to-day.

The seven-day sequence of days that we call the week goes back to very ancient times and appeared in many cultures and religions. It was known in India, Babylonia and Palestine from extremely early days. Its origin may well have been related to the phases of the moon, and there is no doubt it played a large part in astrology. The names of the seven days in many languages reflect the ancients' interest in the seven planets. Panth[2] argues that it may well be an outcome of the setting aside of a regular day for marketing between communities. Ancient Romans observed an eight-day week, and there is evidence that the early Britons knew a five-day cycle.

It is generally accepted that the seven-day week is probably of Semitic origin and certainly it is met early in the Old Testament, where it becomes an important feature of Mosaic law. By the beginning of the Christian era it had been adopted by the Roman empire or was certainly known, but it was not introduced into the

[1] The word perpetualness is not exact, nor does its alternative, perpetuity, suit in describing the situation, but it is the best the author can find for the desirable quality in a calendar of repeating its dates and week-days in a coincident, regular sequence year after year. No annual calendar requiring a quadrennial variation to provide a 'leap' year can be 'perpetual' and the word is used in this book with that reservation.

[2] B. D. Panth, *Consider the Calendar.*

Roman calendar until after the reign of Theodosius (fourth century A.D.). It is however, an arbitrary division of time, having no relation to natural phenomena, except the approximation to the moon's phases. Moreover, it is an illogical arrangement, since it will not divide into equal half-weeks. To Jews it is of course a fundamental part of their calendar, and hardly less so to Christians, some sects of whom do in fact regard any suggestion of revision of the 'seventh day' as irreligious, ignoring the fact that the position of Sundays in the calendar changes every year with respect to the festival of Christmas, one of the two most important religious celebrations.

The Jewish calendar, which has had so close a contact with the Christian, and in its historical context might well have come to be adopted by the early Christians instead of the Julian, is an extremely complicated affair. While the Jewish chronological count goes back directly to the year 3761 B.C., its current form is later than the Julian, being due to Hillel II, Jewish patriarch from A.D. 320 to A.D. 365. It is a luni-solar calendar, based on the Metonic cycle of 19 years, i.e., on the length of the lunation and the tropical year as found by Hipparchus. In a cycle of 19 years, twelve are common years of 354 days (12 lunar months) and seven are embolismic years, i.e., having an added month. These are the 3rd, 6th, 8th, 11th, 14th, 17th and 19th years of the cycle.

It is essentially a religious calendar. 'Before the Christian era, official declarations relating to religious and ceremonial days were made by the Sanhedrin, the Great Council of Jerusalem. These ceremonials have been incorporated in the calendar, which is now so complexly constituted that it is beyond the ken of unschooled laymen'.[1]

Nevertheless it works, and continues to work side by side with the other calendars of the world. For the orthodox Jew

[1] B. D. Panth.

in Britain it involves the suspension of business on what
is his Sabbath but a Christian working day, though
where Jews are in the majority as in the East End of
London, this is compensated by permitting the Jew to
carry on his business on the Christian Sabbath. Jewish
religious holidays, as at the New Year which in a single
19-year cycle can move over the Gregorian period from
September 6 to October 5, are superimposed on the
Gregorian calendar with no more than local or individual inconvenience.

The Julian calendar, minus its Kalends, etc. came to
be accepted and formalized as the Christian calendar in
the time of the Emperor Constantine, and was adopted
at the Christian Council of Nicæa in A.D. 325 (which is
interestingly close to the time when the Jewish patriarch
Hillel was working on the Hebrew system). But it was
not until much later that the era we know as A.D. (Anno
Domini) was established. This was due to the researches
of Dionysius Exiguus, a monk of Scythia who came to
Rome about A.D. 497. He is credited with introducing,
about 525, the method of reckoning years according to a
Christian era, that is from the birth of Christ, which was
designated A.D. 1[1]. The system of describing anterior
dates as 'B.C.', however, was not introduced until much
later. The era most commonly used in Dionysius's day
was the Diocletian era, which the Christians called 'the
era of the martyrs'. It began on August 24, 284.[2]

The calendar had now reverted once more to an
ecclesiastical function, and new complications ensued
with regard to the fixing of the Easter festival. Says
Philip: 'In consequence of the various enactments and
of the general practice of the Church, the seven-day

[1] The historical date is disputed by scholars, and it is now widely
accepted that the more correct date would be that known as 4 B.C.

[2] G. Sarton. Dionysius also fixed March 25 as the beginning of the
Christian year, a practice which continued until the Gregorian reform
of the Julian calendar in 1582.

week, or more correctly the various week-days, acquired
a definite relation to the other elements of the calendar,
which became more stringent through the need which
arose for a calendrial rule to determine the Easter date.
It therefore became necessary to devise a method for
ascertaining for any given year the constantly fluctuating
relation between the week and the month, and in particular for readily ascertaining the calendrial dates of the
Sundays in any particular year.[1] Easter, a 'moveable'
feast, had been ordained to be celebrated on 'the first
Sunday after the first full moon which happens upon, or
next after the 21st March; and if the full moon happens
upon a Sunday, Easter-day is the Sunday after'. It had
and still has a possible range over 35 days.

An ingenious device was invented using what are
known as Dominical Letters or Golden Numbers,[2]
which may be studied in the English Prayer Book, where
advance dates are given for Easter, covering many years.

It may be said that it was the Easter problem which
drew attention to the imperfection of Sosigenes's Julian
calendar as a check on the passing years and gave rise
to the first stirrings in the movement for calendar reform.
Two hundred years had not elapsed after Dionysius's
death before the Venerable Bede (c. 675–735) 'whose
learning was great, covering all the subjects then known'
including astronomy, was writing a treatise on the calendar, dealing with, among other things, the computation
of what came later to be known as the epacts (age of the
moon at the start of the year, important in the working
out of Easter dates) and observing that the equinoxes
were now taking place three days earlier than at the time
of the Council of Nicæa.

He had put his finger on the fault in the Julian calendar,

[1] Alexander Philip, *The Calendar: Its History, Structure and Improvement.*

[2] In the Gregorian reform Epacts were substituted for Golden
Numbers.

the error in the estimate of the length of the tropical year, which of course is not 365¼ days, but 365·2422 days (365 days 5 hours 48 minutes 46 seconds). The difference of 11 minutes and 14 seconds amounts to a whole day in 128 years, and although the Venerable Bede may not have arrived at the exact discrepancy, he had found the approximate figure of adjustment—three days in 400 years—which was to be the key to the Gregorian revision 800 years later.

Much of English and continental learning was devoted to the subject in the next centuries. Innumerable manuscripts bear witness to the concern of philosophers and prelates with the calendar, mainly in the latter case in regard to some aspect of church festivals or procedures, but sometimes in the cause of the advancement of knowledge. It was an age when astrology was more popular than astronomy, and even more credited, but now and again the light broke through. Outstanding names in English scholarship in this connection are Grosseteste, the famous Bishop of Lincoln in the thirteenth century, and the philosopher-scientist Roger Bacon, who suffered imprisonment for his heresies. Bacon's rectified calendar may be seen to-day at Oxford. His treatises on the subject were sent to Pope Clement IV, but no action was taken.

In the meantime the Julian calendar was drifting, at the rate of one day in every 128 years, so that the vernal equinox, which at the time of the Council of Nicæa in A.D. 325 had occurred on March 21 by the Calendar, was slowly changing its date backwards through the month, thus:

In A.D.   325 the spring equinox occurred on March 21
In A.D.   453 the spring equinox occurred on March 20
In A.D.   581 the spring equinox occurred on March 19
In A.D.   709 the spring equinox occurred on March 18
In A.D.   837 the spring equinox occurred on March 17
In A.D.   965 the spring equinox occurred on March 16

In A.D. 1093 the spring equinox occurred on March 15
In A.D. 1221 the spring equinox occurred on March 14
In A.D. 1349 the spring equinox occurred on March 13
In A.D. 1477 the spring equinox occurred on March 12

By the sixteenth century, therefore, it had moved a space of ten days.

What concerned the church was that, since Easter was tied to March 21, the date in 325 of the spring equinox (equal night and day), that festival was slowly moving out of the proper season.

In time, if it were left alone, the equinox would occur in February, then in January, and so on, while the nominal date of March 21, and consequently Easter, and its appendix Whitsuntide, would advance into the summer.

There was a strong movement for reform at the Council of Constance in 1417, when Cardinal Pierre d'Ailly, Chancellor of the University of Paris, delivered a learned disquisition on the subject, quoting Grosseteste. Thirty years later, at the Council of Basle, the German Cardinal Nicolaus Cusa in 1436 put forward a plan for dropping a number of days from the calendar, but it was nearly another half-century before the Church itself took the matter in hand, and Pope Sixtus IV called in the German astronomer Regiomontanus, author of the first printed almanac (1474), for advice.[1] Regiomontanus unfortunately died in the next year, and the matter was again put off, although a number of works criticising the calendar appeared. At last the subject came up again at the Council of Trent (1545–63), but it was not until the time of Pope Gregory XIII that action was taken.

One of the first acts of Pope Gregory XIII on his assumption of office in 1572 must have been to gather to his court some of the famous astronomers of the day, notably Luigi Lilio

[1] Bertha M. Frick, in *Journal of Calendar Reform*, 1943.

(Aloysius Lilius) and his brother, Antonio, to set them to work on a new calendar. A plan was finally drawn up which recommended the dropping of ten days, in order to restore the equinoxes to their true date, and to count century years as intercalary only if they were divisible by 400. So drastic an act as to destroy ten days must have made even the Pope wonder whether his power and influence were great enough to carry it through. As a preliminary and precautionary measure, in 1577 Gregory sent letters to various Catholic princes of Europe and to outstanding universities stating the need of reform and enclosing a draft of the measures proposed by Lilio and approved by a committee at Rome. What consternation his communication must have caused![1]

What consternation, indeed. It was an extraordinary plan, but something like it was the only practical solution. It went through, and in 1581 the historic papal bull was published which decreed that in the following year the days between October 5 and 14 were to be omitted from all calendars and almanacs. Creditors were to 'take account of this time and add ten days at the end of the periods when loans would become due'. Printing of the new calendar was forbidden to any but officially dessignated printers 'lest errors be made' under penalty of fines and even excommunication 'no matter what part of the world they may be in'. The edict was to be posted on the doors of all churches and inserted in all volumes containing 'Calendaria' and 'Martyrologia'. In the following year the full official version was published, and Antonio Lilio (his brother Luigi had died) was given exclusive printing rights for ten years.

That, then, was the beginning of the Gregorian calendar; the first essential change (excepting the introduction of the week) in the Julian system for 1,600 years. But it was not destined to have a smooth passage. There was a storm of protest, ecclesiastical and lay. The Roman

[1] Bertha M. Frick.

Catholic countries accepted it—they could not do otherwise—but not the Eastern Orthodox nations, nor the Protestants, who labelled it 'Popery'. It was to require three centuries and more to overcome the prejudices which arrayed themselves against this entirely sensible, and indeed inevitable, correction in the measurement of time.

CHAPTER V

Two Earls and an Astronomer

IF IT IS TRUE, as is so often adumbrated, that
'the time produces the man', in this case time was long
enough about it. While navigation and knowledge were
both improving and tending to bring the nations to a
closer acquaintance (if not always a closer friendship),
their calendars were drifting steadily a little farther
apart and tending equally to widen their separation. In
the year 1700, when the first of the leap year days under
the Gregorian rule was dropped from the continental
calendar, but observed in Britain, the difference of ten
days became eleven. The thing applied also in the new
world. The English colonies in North America were
employing one calendar; the Spanish and Portuguese
countries in South America another.

The whole thing seems extraordinarily incongruous
now, but the situation continued for more than a century
and a half, sustained by prejudice and the lack of any
determined effort to change it. What was required was
that the anomaly should be tackled by someone with
great enough influence and at the same time technical
knowledge of the subject to focus the need for change
and enforce it. The fog of prejudice and the haziness
and laziness of general thinking on the matter had
simultaneously to be penetrated.

The man who finally took the matter into his capable
and subtle hands, as the eighteenth century touched its
half-way mark, was the then Earl of Chesterfield, a man

who combined in his single person all the qualities and experience of politician, diplomat, courtier, wit, scholar and Parliamentarian. And to collaborate with him on the technical aspects of the undertaking was another distinguished figure in the person of the Earl of Macclesfield, a peer celebrated for his scientific attainments; and also the then Astronomer Royal, James Bradley.

With Chesterfield as leader, these three broke through the entrenched ranks of prejudice with what might almost be called a lightning attack, and the reform was brought about before the ancient opposition had time to coalesce and organize a counter-attack.

The story of how it was done cannot be better summarized than in a volume of *Parliamentary History*, that reportorial predecessor of Hansard, which, as a footnote to its report of 'Proceedings in the Lords on the Bill for regulating the Commencement of the Year and for correcting the Calendar now in use', quotes the following extract from Dr. Maty's Memoirs of Lord Chesterfield:

Lord Chesterfield, who always had the honour, as well as the advantage of his country in view, had long deplored that Great Britain should be almost the last of all the European powers which still persisted in the use of the defective Julian calendar. Neither the scruples which it occasioned among zealous churchmen concerning the true time of the principal anniversary festivals, nor even its considerable and increasing disagreement from the heavenly bodies (a circumstance, on account of the slowness of its progression, perceptible only to astronomers), were perhaps, the chief motives that induced Lord Chesterfield to wish for a reformation; but he was more particularly disposed to encourage it from the confusion which the different beginnings of the year might produce in settling historical transactions, and the variance there was in the accounts of almost every other state. The inconveniences were evident, and the difficulty of obviating several inconveniences attending a sudden alteration, and especially in overcoming people's prejudices, were not less so. These difficulties he found still more considerable than he imagined.

Having consulted the duke of Newcastle; that minister, then in the zenith of his power, seemed alarmed at so bold an undertaking. He conjured the earl not to stir matters that had long been quiet, and added, that he did not love new-fangled things. Lord Chesterfield, however, did not suffer himself to be deterred by these obstacles, but resolved to digest his plan thoroughly before he communicated it to the public.

With regard to the civil and political points, he consulted persons of the greatest eminence in the several parts of the world where he maintained a correspondence. He was particularly obliged to the great chancellor Pagessau for the most useful information, and received from him a most instructive letter on the subject, which we regret much not to be able to give to the public. In the astronomical part, he consulted those of his countrymen who were most in repute for their knowledge in that science; and particularly the earl of Macclesfield, then president of the Royal Society, who readily entered into the plan of reforming the calendar, and furnishing Lord Chesterfield with all the learning that was wanted on the occasion.

Thus prepared, our earl made his motion in the House of Lords, on the 25th of February of that style he wished to amend. The speech he made on that occasion was entirely calculated to captivate the attention and secure the favour of his hearers. Witty reflections upon time, its measure, though fixed in itself, still dependent on the variable motions of the celestial bodies, a concise and clear account of the several attempts made at different periods, and by different nations, to reconcile those two measures with one another; the inconvenience attending the present stile, with respect to all public and private transactions; the method of obviating the difficulties arising from a sudden alteration: these were the principal topics which he dwelt upon. He displayed such powers of oratory in this speech, and delivered it with so much grace, that he eclipsed lord Macclesfield, who seconded his motion, and, in a speech previously prepared and since printed, entered much more fully into the argumentative part of the plan.

Our earl did ample justice to his learned colleague: and in his familiar letters expressed himself with great modesty on this point, attributing entirely to his powers of utterance the advantage he obtained over him on this occasion. A Bill so wisely contrived, and so ably supported by eloquence and reason, passed without any opposition in both Houses; but those who now enjoy the advantages resulting from it, ought to be informed, that they owe them to the industry and resolution of the earl of Chesterfield.

Just when Chesterfield's interest in the subject began or when action was decided on is not clear, but there could have been no one at the time to whom the dual calendar problem was more persistently present, for it was at this time that the noble Earl was writing, every few weeks, those delightfully paternal letters of guidance and advice to the young man who was being educated in Germany, in Italy and in France. That the chronological order of these missives and their replies should not seem inconsistent it was as necessary for the Earl to add the letters O.S. (Old Style) to the date of his writings as it was for the answers, sent from the continent, to carry the indication N.S. (New Style). There is for example a letter dated 'Greenwich, June 6, O.S. 1751' which, towards its end says: 'This moment I receive your letter of the 9th N.S.' which, without the indication of the style, would create the absurd situation that the young man's message had arrived three days before it was written. So long as the style was indicated, however, it is clear enough; but to this day writers dealing with the period have to wrestle with the complication whenever they dig down to original documents.

Few people therefore could have been more continuously conscious of the anomaly, and it was at the same time a convenient interlude in the Earl's hitherto busy life which gave him the opportunity to take up this cause of correction that already so frequently had failed. At the turn of the half-century he was unpopular at Court, had become badly incapacitated by deafness, and except for attendance from time to time at the House of

Lords, had virtually retired from public life. So his action in 1751 in bringing in his Bill for the reform of the calendar, in the words of one historian, 'did him honour on many accounts; for the difficulties of detail were great, and the prejudices against it strong'.

It was in his interesting letter, the acme of modesty, dated 'London, March 18, O.S. 1751' that his lordship told the story of how it came about. 'I acquainted you in a former letter', he wrote to his son, 'that I had brought a bill into the House of Lords, for correcting and reforming our present calendar, which is the Julian, and for adopting the Gregorian. I will now give you a more particular account of that affair, from which reflections will naturally occur to you that I hope may be useful, and which I fear you have not made.

It was notorious, that the Julian calendar was erroneous, and had overcharged the solar year with eleven days. Pope Gregory XIII corrected this error; his reformed calendar was immediately received by all the Catholic Powers of Europe, and afterwards adopted by all the Protestant ones, except Russia, Sweden and England. It was not, in my opinion, very honourable for England to remain in a gross and avowed error, especially in such company; the inconvenience of it was likewise felt by all those who had foreign correspondences, whether political or mercantile. I determined, therefore, to attempt the reformation; I consulted the best lawyers, and the most skilful astronomers, and we cooked up a bill for that purpose. But then my difficulty began; I was to bring in this bill, which was necessarily composed of law jargon and astronomical calculations to both of which I am an utter stranger. However, it was absolutely necessary to make the House of Lords think that I knew something of the matter, and also to make them believe that they knew something of it themselves, which they do not. For my own part, I could just as soon have talked Celtic or Sclavonian to them as astronomy, and they would have understood me full as well; so I resolved to do better than speak to the purpose, and to please instead of informing them. I gave them, therefore, only an historical account of calendars, from

the Egyptian down to the Gregorian, amusing them now and
then with little episodes; but I was particularly attentive to
the choice of my words, to the harmony and roundness of my
periods, to my elocution, to my action. This succeeded, and
ever will succeed; they thought I informed, because I pleased
them; and many of them said, that I had made the whole very
clear to them, when, God knows, I had not even attempted it.
Lord Macclesfield, who had the greatest share in forming the
Bill, and who is one of the greatest mathematicians and
astronomers in Europe, spoke afterwards with infinite knowledge, and all the clearness that so intricate a matter would
admit of, but as his words, his periods, and his utterances were
not near so good as mine, the preference was most unanimously, though most unjustly, given to me.

Such at last, then, was the action which brought the
English calendar into line with the continental, and
although it had perhaps no direct bearing on the chronological story, it is an amusing commentary on Lord
Chesterfield's general attitude to his contemporary peers
that his letter continued:

This will ever be the case; every numerous assembly is *mob*
let the individuals who compose it be what they will. Mere
reason and good sense is never to be talked to a mob; their
passions, their sentiments, their senses, and their seeming
interests, are alone to be applied to. Understanding they have
collectively none; but they have ears and eyes, which must be
flattered and seduced; and this can only be done by eloquence,
tuneful periods, graceful action, and all the various parts of
oratory.

This philosophy fitted well enough into the Earl's
purpose at the time, for it must be remembered that he
was then—and indeed throughout his *Letters*—trying to
instil into his not too bright son the principles and graces
of eminence; but had he not held such opinions and put
them into practice, it may be that England, like Russia,
Turkey and other countries, would have gone on suffering under this calendrical disability into the present

century, by which time the disagreement in the two calendars amounted to 13 days. It is not even certain that it would have been done yet.

Unfortunately there was no Hansard in those days and so no full record of the Chesterfield dissertation, but that it was brilliant, witty and delightful, and informative to boot, is agreed by all contemporary historians. It must indeed have put the House into a suitable and receptive mood for the serious discourse which was to follow: that of the distinguished Earl of Macclesfield, scientist, mathematician, astronomer, whose learning was such that later that year he was unanimously elected President of the Royal Society.

Macclesfield's address was a sober affair compared with that of his elegant predecessor. If Chesterfield had given the peers the romantic side of the story his colleague dealt with the realistic, and he gave them the scientific and astronomical facts as well as the weighty reasons of convenience behind the measure. And, as Chesterfield politely gave credit to Macclesfield for an alleged greater share in the task, so the latter in turn acknowledged the important parts taken in the campaign by others.

'This Bill was, under his lordship's (Chesterfield's) direction', he said, 'drawn and most of the tables prepared by Davall, a barrister of the Middle Temple, whose skill in astronomy, as well as in his profession, rendered him extremely capable of accurately performing that work; which was likewise carefully examined, and approved of, by two gentlemen, whose learning and abilities are so well known, that nothing which I can say can add to their characters: I mean Mr. Ffolkes, president of the Royal Society; and Dr. Bradley, his majesty's astronomer at Greenwich; the latter of whom did himself compose the three general tables, which your lordships find towards the end of the printed copy'.

So the Bill that Chesterfield and his friends had

'cooked up', as the Earl merrily put it, came into being, and thanks to the manner of its presentation met with readier success than its sponsors could reasonably have hoped for, in view of the bigoted opposition of the past. It passed with unusual speed through both Houses, and whereas in its issue dated March 2 1751, the newspaper *Old England* had dealt with the whole affair in a two-line paragraph which said merely:

> Monday the Bill for altering our Stile
> was brought into the House of Peers,

the same newspaper, a four-page sheet published by 'Argus Centoculi, Inspector-General of Great Britain' carried in its issue of May 25 in that same year the imposing announcement that:

> Wednesday his Majesty went to the House of Peers in his State Coach, attended by the Earl Waldegrave and Lord Cathcart and being seated on the Throne, and Sir Harry Ballendine, Usher of the Black Rod, having by order of his Majesty commanded the Commons Attendance, his Majesty gave the Royal assent to the following Bills,

one of which was the Bill 'for correcting the Style, and regulating the Calendar now in use'. Incidentally, it is notable in passing that here appears to be the first time in reference to this Act that the word so commonly used to describe the calendar acquired its modern spelling 'Style', though in other places it continued to be spelled 'Stile' for some time.

The whole affair then had gone through from introduction to Royal Assent within less than three months. Now the country had to prepare itself to drop eleven days completely from the calendar in September of the next year, and printers and historians alike could rejoice that at last the date of the start of the year was to be established firmly so that there could be no equivocation

E

as to whether any January, February or March fell in, say, 1751 or 1752, as so long there had been.

This question of the double date had been a frequent source of irritation, as we have seen, but once dealt with by this new statute it could occasion no further trouble, and at least the years would in future agree throughout Christendom. But the remainder of the Act had trouble enough in store, though this in fact did not seem to call forth such immediate outcry as might well have been expected, and as it would certainly have done in modern times. Rather, the Press of the period seems to have lain low and waited.

It was in the September of the year 1752 that the storm was scheduled to break. In that month, to pull the English calendar into line with the Continental, i.e. to convert the Julian to the Gregorian, eleven days were to disappear completely, to vanish into thin air, to be treated as though they did not exist—indeed, they were forbidden to exist. One day—a Wednesday—would be the 2nd of September, the next—the Thursday—was be the 14th. It had its absurd side, but there it was. It had to be done.

What comment there was on the passing of the Act seemed all to be on the lighter side, and if opposition did not immediately make itself evident, there were those who found it a subject for their wit. One such was no less distinguished a commentator than the famous writer (though not yet Dr.) Samuel Johnson. It was just at this period that he was publishing his short-lived weekly, *The Rambler*, devoted to highly moral and elevating disquisitions on current affairs. Less elevating was a letter purporting to be from a young girl who signed herself 'Properantia' which appeared in the issue of the journal dated March 26 1751. However, there is no proof that Johnson wrote it—nor is there any that he did not.

To the Rambler. Dear Sir (it reads)
Though as my mamma tells me, I am too young to talk at

the table, I have great pleasure in listening to the conversation of learned men, especially when they discourse of things which I do not understand, and have, therefore, been of late particularly delighted with many disputes about the *alteration of the stile*, which, they say, is to be done by act of parliament.

One day, when my mamma was gone out of the room, I asked a very great scholar what the *stile* was. He told me, he was afraid I should hardly understand him when he informed me that it was the stated and established method of computing time. It was not, indeed, likely that I should understand him: for, I never yet knew time computed in my life, nor can imagine why we should be at such trouble to count what we cannot keep. He did not tell me whether we are to count the time past, or the time to come; but I have considered them both by myself, and think it as foolish to count time that is gone, as money that is spent; and as for the time which is to come, it only seems farther off by counting, and therefore when any pleasure is promised me, I always think as little of the time as I can.

I have since listened very attentively to every one that talked upon this subject, of whom the greater part seem not to understand it better than myself; for though they often hint how much the nation has been mistaken, and rejoice that we are at last growing wiser than our ancestors, I have never been able to discover from them, that anybody has died the sooner for counting time wrong; and, therefore, I began to fancy that there was great battle with little consequences.

At last two friends of my pappa, Mr. Cycle and Mr. Starlight, being, it seems, both of high learning, and able to make an almanack, began to talk about the new stile. Sweet Mr. Starlight—I am sure I shall love this name as long as I live, for he told Cycle roundly, with a fierce look, that we should never be right without a *year of confusion*.

Dear Mr. Rambler, did you ever hear anything so charming? A whole year of confusion! When there has been a rout at mamma's I have thought one night of confusion worth a thousand nights of rest; and surely if I can but see a year of confusions, a whole year, of cards in one room, and dancing in another, here a feast, and there a masquerade, and plays and coaches, and hurries, and messages, and milleners, and raps at the door, and visits and frolicks, and *new* fashions, I shall not care what they do with the rest of the time, nor whether they count it to be the old stile or the new, for I am resolved to break loose from the nursery in the tumult, and play my part among the rest; and it will be strange if I cannot get a husband and a chariot in the year of confusion.

Cycle, who is neither so young, nor so handsome as Starlight, very gravely maintained, that all the perplexity may be avoided by leaping over eleven days in the reckoning; and indeed if it should come only to this, I think the new stile is a delightful thing; for my mamma says that I shall go to court when I am sixteen, and if they can but contrive to leap over eleven days together, the months of restraint will be soon at an end. It is strange that with all the plots that have been laid against time, they could never kill it by act of parliament before.

Dear sir, if you have any vote or any interest, get them but for once to destroy eleven months, and then I shall be as old as some married ladies. But this is desired only if you think they will not comply with Mr. Starlight's scheme, for nothing surely would please me like a year of confusion, when I shall no longer be fixed this hour to my pen and the next to my needle, and wait at home for the dancing master one day, and the next for the musick master, but run from ball to ball, and from drum to drum, and spend all my time without tasks, and without account, and go out without telling whither, and come home without regard to prescribed hours or family rules. I am, etc. PROPERANTIA.

Just whom the sweet little Miss Properantia was supposed to be referring to is not very clear, but, since they were both 'able to make an almanack', they were possibly Bradley and Macclesfield, but the 'year of confusion' was clear enough as a reference to the historic period of Julius Cæsar's reform, which must at this time have been recalled frequently by all whose history was equal to the occasion.

Argus Centoculi, the 'author', as editors or editor-proprietors of newspapers at the time described themselves, of *Old England*, also found in the Act a target for his wit.

We have an old saying concerning the British Parliament, he wrote, 'that it can do anything bar change a Man into a Woman; intimating that this Assembly hath as much Power as anyone that ever existed: For the Experiment of making a Permutation of the Sexes was never, that we know of, attempted by any human authority. . . .

Our history affords abundant Instances of Kings, that were made and unmade. . . . Our religion has been changed by the same Authority. . . . Our Constitution has undergone many Mutations in consequence of the same uncontrollable Power. . . . Who, that has seen the great Alteration lately made in our Funds, by the Reduction of the National Interest, can dispute the Authority of a British Parliament? . . . The Bill which, as the public Papers assure us, has been brought into the Upper House . . . for altering the Old Julian Stile, which, ever since the Roman Conquest, has been used in these islands, is an instance of the most extraordinary changes that may be affected by the Authority of which we are speaking. . . .

It is not within the Competency of Man, however dignified or authorized, actually to stay the Steps of Time, or to anticipate him in his Career: But this instance will show us, that there is a kind of Power of overtaking him, at least in Computation, practicable, when he has got too far the Start of us, in his annual Course. . . .

But I did not propose, when I first entered upon this Subject (Centoculi goes on after much more to the same purpose), to begin a serious Dissertation on the Alteration of our Stile. My principal View was to consider in what Manner and Degree, this Alteration would affect my Readers, especially the fair Part of them, for whom I have always the most profound Respect. . . . I am now impelled to give them Notice of an Effect, which will reach them, by the Law at present under Consideration, and of which I conceive not many of them are apprised. It is, that this Change of the Stile will cause the Anticipation of their usual Reckoning, and precipitate them 11 days sooner than they expected, into the state that is most

dreadful to a fair lady, Virgin, Wife, or Widow; I mean the
State of old Age.

It will be vain to keep double Reckonings, in order to ward
off this Misfortune, when the Law itself is calculated for no
other purpose than to present a Multiplicity of Accounts.
I know no other Remedy therefore, in this Case, for any
lovely Female, whose Birthday is already known, than a
patient submission to a Law, which, however cruelly it may
affect them, is doubtless intended, upon the whole, for general
Benefit: And, as a patriotic Spirit has of late years taken
Possession of many of the softer Sex, I doubt not but it will
influence them on this Occasion, to submit with proper
Resignation. . . .

CHAPTER VI

The Eleven Days

THAT MONTH of September 1752 was the shortest in English or any other history; shorter than even the ancient Aztec month of 20 days,[1] for it contained only 19. It looked like this:

S	M	T	W	T	F	S
		1	2	14	15	16
17	18	19	20	21	22	23
24	25	26	27	28	29	30

and the whole year contained only 355 days (it was a leap year), which was only one day more than the normal Moslem year. Also the month began and ended within two days less than three weeks.

All this was undoubtedly confusing at the time and one can easily imagine that it led to considerable disturbance and irritation. Just how much disturbance, however, it is not now easy to ascertain. It is widely held that outbreaks, riots and even deaths were occasioned by it, but it would seem that over the years the stories of such disturbances as might have happened have possibly become more dramatic through repetition and exaggeration. The present writer has sought to confirm the tales of 'riots' from many likely sources of information, but without success.

More than one historian, for example, has mentioned 'London and Bristol' specifically as the scenes of

[1] See Chapter 3.

63

riots and of mobs crying 'Give us back our eleven days!' Though I looked into what seemed likely records at Guildhall, the Public Record Office and in contemporary newspapers at the British Museum, I discovered no support for this popularly held opinion so far as London was concerned. As to Bristol, I had the courteous aid of the City Archivist there, who wrote:

> I have searched the City records including the Minutes of the Common Council but can find no evidence that there were any serious disturbances in Bristol occasioned by this reform. Mention is made of it in the Minutes of the 21st March 1752 where it was stated 'Mr. Mayor acquainted the House that by the late Act of Parliament for regulating the commencement of the year, and for correcting the Calendar now in use; eleven days were deducted out of the present year, And moved that Mr. Chamberlain might be impowered to make the proper allowance for time to the Tenents holding under this Corporation, on that account. . . ." No reference to it occurs in any of the calendar histories of Bristol.
>
> At the Quarter Sessions of the 31st August 1753 several people were accused of felony and of 'misdemeanors relating to the late Riots'. This, however, refers to the insurrection amongst the colliers in Kingswood who rioted on account of the dearness of bread and did much damage to the city.

So it seems that the only riots Bristol suffered around that time had no concern with the calendar, at least directly, and, according to Professor Aspinall, of Reading University, who also lent kindly assistance, Lecky, the great historian of the period, referred to no more than 'widespread irritation', arising out of the confusion. In other populous centres there may have been more serious consequences, but on the whole it would seem that whatever demonstrations may have taken place—and this is not to say that none did—were confined probably to general grumbling and raised voices at meetings and in drinking dens and at political gatherings. There is certainly support for strong feelings finding an outlet in such places and on such occasions as these in the famous contemporary Hogarth picture of 'The Election', in which the artist depicts a carousal in the parlour of an inn with three significant indications of the party's politics: a slashed picture of the King, a flag emblazoned 'Liberty and Loyalty' and another, lying on the ground, bearing the slogan 'Give us our Eleven Days'.

However, riots or no riots, it would be hard to believe that so drastic a social change could be carried through without trouble. It must have had its awkward effects on innumerable transactions and events, and probably the theme of the eleven missing days did punctuate political meetings and provide useful fuel for stump orators for years afterwards. In the meantime, the problem was how to adjust wages, rents and such-like payments. If Lord Chesterfield had said he couldn't understand it, what were ordinary people to make of this extraordinary situation —one day the 2nd of September, and the next the 14th?

True, the Act had provided that 'nothing is intended to extend, to accelerate or anticipate the time of payment of any rent, annuity or sum of money . . .' and gone into great detail about putting forward dates of 'markets, fairs and marts, and courts thereon depending . . .' and the 'opening, inclosing or shutting up any lands or common pasture according to divers customs, privileges and usages . . .' but there were those who believed that not only were they losing eleven days' wages, but that their lives were being shortened. Partly this problem was solved by the printing, in all the newspapers of the period, of tables showing the deductions which could be made from monthly and annual wages or payments to adjust them to the shorter term; but that did not satisfy those who objected on religious grounds, as is shown by the following note published in *Felix Farley's Journal*, the contemporary Bristol newspaper, on January 6 1753:

Yesterday being Old Christmas Day, the same was obstinately observed by our country people in general; so that yesterday (which was Market Day by order of our Magistrates) there were but few at Market, who embraced the opportunity of raising their butter to 9d. or 10d. a pound

—which was about double the usual price. In some market towns, says one authority,[1] the farmers were wholly absent; and to gratify the feelings of their parishioners many rural clergymen preached 'Nativity sermons' on the following Sunday. The extent to which the religious aspect of the reform was called into question and the persistence of the opposition are illustrated by the story of the 'Glastonbury thorn' related by Latimer:

The flowering of the celebrated Glastonbury thorn was looked for with much anxiety. The first intelligence of its deportment gave satisfaction, the above newspaper (*Felix Farley's Journal*) confirming that the holy plant, after having contemptuously ignored the new style, burst into blossom on the 5th January, thus indicating that Old Christmas Day should alone be observed in spite of an irreligious legislature.

This story, strange to say, was printed at Hull for the use of 'flying stationers' who then traversed the country, and produced an immense effect in the rural district. Eventually, some one thought it worth while to write to the vicar of Glastonbury, and the emptiness of the report was at once made known, the reverend gentleman declaring that the thorn 'blossomed the fullest and finest about Christmas Day, new style, or rather sooner'. As farmers and labourers were not newspaper readers, however, their faith in the fable was transmitted to their descendants. Mr. Humphries, in his *History of Wellington*, published in 1889, states that many of the labouring classes in that neighbourhood still strictly observe Old Christmas Day, believing that it would be wicked to work on the ancient festival'.

On the other hand, there were those who treated the whole matter as an immense joke, as in the following letter which appeared in the September 1752 issue of

[1] John Latimer, *The Annals of Bristol in the Eighteenth Century* (1893), p. 298.

the *Gentleman's Magazine*, quoted, apparently, from another journal called *The Inspector*:

Mr. Inspector, I write to you in the greatest perplexity. I desire you'll find some way of setting my affairs to rights: or I believe I shall run mad, and break my heart into the bargain. How is all this? I desire to know finally and truly! I went to bed last night, it was *Wednesday, Sept. 2*, and the first thing I cast my eye upon this morning at the top of your paper, was *Thursday, Sept. 14*. I did not go to bed till between one and two: Have I slept away 11 days in 7 hours, or how is it? For my part, I don't find I'm any more refresh'd than after a common night's sleep.

They tell me there's an act of parliament for this. With due reverence be it spoken, I have always thought there were very few things a *British* parliament could not do, but if I had been asked, I should have guessed the annihilation of time was not one of them!

How apt are we to laugh at things only because we don't understand 'em. *Ye gods annihilate but space and time, and make two lovers happy!* I remember the days, Sir, when we have laughed at this as an extravagant conception: but time discovers all things. The *British* parliament, without the help of gods or devils either, has accomplished one half of the miracle, and I'm convinced it will be found as easy to bring about the other.

One thing, however, I can assure you has surprised me very much, that his majesty[1] should consent to it, since he is plainly robb'd by it of 11 days out of the time he was to spend in his *German* dominions: but he is a patriotic prince, and there is nothing he will refuse that is for the good of his people. The next exploit of our superiors may be the annihilation of space, and *Hanover* and *London* will lie together. That the lawyers will concur in this, I do not wonder: fine work it will doubtless make in Westminster Hall, in spite of all the provision that is made against it. But that the bench of bishops should agree to it, is I confess, an astonishment to me. What do their reverences intend to do about St. Emerchus? Who he was I don't know, nor I suppose you nor they either; but that's

[1] George II.

neither here nor there; you'll find him in your prayer book; look into the calendar, and his name stands right against the seventh of *September*. I don't know whether I'm right awake, but now there's no seventh of *September* this year; and I don't know what title they or any body of men in the world could have to rob him of his anniversary. The very next day to it is the *Nativity of Mary*: just in the same situation again! I suppose she was to be born no day at all this year. A strange liberty tho' this, to be taken with people that they pretend to have respect for!

Apropo! The talking of her birthday puts me in mind of my own. You that have been all the while in *England* may be prepared for the thing, and it mayn't affect you so particularly; but, Sir, I have not been six weeks arrived from the *West Indies*, and knew nothing of the matter till it came plump upon me this morning. I really thought at first sight, that I had slept almost a fortnight.

The perplexity it makes in my affairs is beyond describing. I have lost a considerable bet by it; I have disappointed myself in the most cruel manner in the world; and all I don't know how, nor why, nor wherefore. I used to laugh at a man of my acquaintance for having a birthday but once in three years;[1] because it fell on the 29th February: he laid me a considerable wager one of these nights, that I should lose a birthday some year or other as a punishment for my mockery. He was drunk when he made the proposal, but I little thought I should live to see it demanded. Sir, I am born on the 13th day of September so that by good rights I should have kept my birthday last night at supper time, it was the eve of the fourteenth, I am sure, if there was any. I have been always used, on that day of the month, Sir, to give my friends a turtle at the mitre; my cards were sent out in time as usual; and the turtle will be ready. I desire you will tell me when it is to be dressed, and come and eat some of it for your pains.

But must I confess the fatal truth to you? Sir, I have solicited the most amiable of her sex these five weeks: she seemed for a long time only to laugh at me, though my fortune is equal to her own; at last, Sir, she fixed the day, for the tenth of *September*, and she gave me a bond of ten thousand

[1] The writer obviously meant every fourth year.

pounds for the performance. I have consulted my lawyer; he is now at breakfast with me; and he says it will not do for next year, because the date 1752 is fixed to it: and so my ten thousand pounds are not worth ten pence. A fine affair, Sir, that a man must be cheated out of his wife by a parcel of *Mackematicians* and *almanack makers*, before he has her: a new sort of divorce truly: But however, it is by Parliament.

I don't know how to relish this marriage in the *Greek Calendar* I assure you; this payment at *latter Lammas*,—For that matter it's wet enough and its cold enough for any 14th of *September* in *England*; and I believe this really may be the fourteenth in matter of fact, and that we have been putting *Michaelmas* backward and backward these five hundred years: but why it should come to be set right just to put off my marriage I cannot find out, and I must say I think I have a right to speak as a sufferer.

In fine, Mr. Inspector, I apply to you as a person of interest as well as discretion; and as I can think of no relief but by applying to the parliament in favour of my contract, I shall request of you to print my memorial, which I will transmit to you as soon as it can be written out fair, and to employ your utmost endeavours to procure me the proper redress. It is not such a great deal that I ask, it is only a wife. The parliament have divided many a couple, I think it would not be a bad example if they brought one pair together. I know you won't refuse me your interest, because I am confident I have the right on my side; and I beg you will exert it strenuously, unless you may think I am as well without her: but this and all other considerations I leave to your superior wisdom, and am with all respect and submission,

Your most perplexed and confounded humble servant,

R.R.

P.S. Under favour, I do not know if I have not thought of an expedient that will set it right on all sides. *February* has been scratched off a day or two these many years: suppose you apply to have the eleven days added to the end of that month, and so for once make it consist of nine and thirty or forty, its only calling them the third, fourth, etc. of September, 1752, and we are all right again,

This postscript, so merrily written by 'R.R.' is probably the only proposal for calendar reform made in so jocular a spirit, but he seemed to have overlooked that the Act had even taken care of the birthday problem, for its last paragraph, before setting out long new Easter Tables, reads:

> . . . and that no person shall be deemed to have attained the age of 21 years, or any such other age as beforementioned, or to have completed the time of any service as beforementioned, until the full number of years and days shall be elapsed, on which such person or persons respectively would have attained such age, or have completed the time of such service, in case no alteration of the style had been proposed or enacted.

CHAPTER VII

The Maryland Mystery

WHEN POPE GREGORY had issued his famous Bull *Inter Gravissimus* in 1582 he had not converted the world to calendar reform. Probably the world, as such, was little interested. What he had done was to impose a new time-denominational system on those countries which acknowledged his authority in both ecclesiastical and civil affairs. Beneficient as it was in purpose and in fact, the interregnum between its promulgation in Rome and its adoption by the various states and nations varied very widely. It was to be 170 years before Britain came into line.

However, where the Papal authority was uncontested, steps were taken immediately to adopt the new plan. France, Spain, Portugal and Italy were first to fall into line, although not all Italy. An English newspaper of 1751 reported under the heading 'Italy' that 'His imperial majesty, as grand duke of Tuscany . . . has abolished the old stile of his grand duchy, where till now it had continued, in the neighbourhood of Rome, ever since Pope Gregory's reformation, which is at last received'.

Switzerland, the Catholic Netherlands and Flanders put the reformed calendar into force on January 1 1583, and were closely followed by Poland in 1586, Hungary 1587. Then there was a long break before the Protestant States of Germany, inspired mainly by the philosopher Leibnitz, made this particular concession to progress in

1699, and then Denmark in 1700. In the meantime, it is worth noting that Scotland had, exactly a century earlier, made its year begin on January 1, while England was still continuing—and was to continue for another 150 years—to start the year on March 25. This change, though not strictly a part of the Gregorian reform, was later to be adopted together with it.

Sweden made a very clever move. In deciding to give way, in the early part of the eighteenth century, to the demand that its calendar should agree with those of its European neighbours, it planned the change without the disruption of dates which had necessarily ensued elsewhere when ten days had suddenly to be dropped. Instead, Sweden neatly omitted the leap year days from the Julian calendar until a sufficient number of years had gone by to bring the old time-table back into step with the new. It took from 1700 to 1740 to complete the adjustment. Thus Sweden was the one country to adopt reform in a smooth and gradual manner, compared with the drastic hiatus the Papal edict had called for. The Swedish scheme was however originally an English idea, for it had been mooted by John Greaves, an Oxford Professor of Astronomy, in 1645.

But although the German and Scandinavian states bowed after a while to the inevitable, neither Protestants, the Eastern Orthodox Church, nor Mohammedans, nor adherents of any other religions liked it. England turned her face sharply against it. Elizabeth I, it is recorded, called in that strange romantic figure of the time, the mathematician and astrologer John Dee, for advice. Dr. Dee was in favour, and the Queen agreed, but the prelates objected strongly to the adoption of the Catholic innovation, and Elizabeth gave way. Dee had suggested the novel idea of distributing the ten days' alteration over the summer months of a single year, adjusting the months so that May, July and August would each have 29 days, and June would have 28 in that year. A Bill was

IS IT THE WORLD'S OLDEST CALENDAR?

Countless centuries ago, and before the Flood, according to a modern theory, there existed the Sacred City of Tiahuanaco in the Bolivian Andes where the Sun was worshipped in the magnificent Temple of Kalasasaya. This monolithic relic is believed to have been the Gateway to the Temple and its sculpture to indicate its period. It is held that it records a time when there existed a moon before our present moon and when the day was actually longer than the month.

'GIVE US OUR ELEVEN DAYS'

Part of the celebrated painting by Hogarth, one of a series entitled
The Election, now in the Sir John Soane Museum, Lincoln's Inn Fields,
London, in which the artist immortalised the political Battle of the
Calendar in the middle of the eighteenth century. 'Give us Our Eleven Days'
was the popular slogan emblazoned on the flag—an appeal as hopeless
as was evidently the condition of the man who displayed it.

in fact presented to Parliament to this effect in 1585, but it got no farther than second reading.

So England, through war and peace, had during the whole of the seventeenth and half of the eighteenth century to carry on in the anomalous situation of having a calendar that differed at first ten days and then (after 1700 when the first of the Gregorian leap year days was dropped) eleven days out of step with that of its nearest neighbours. It also had, for civil purposes, a different starting for the year, so that for three months each year the English and continental dates became steadily more intolerable to intelligent people. From time to time agitations were begun to overcome religious prejudice and have the English calendar brought into line. There was one originating in Oxford in 1645; another was set on foot by the Royal Society in 1699, and the matter must frequently have been debated in learned circles everywhere.

In 1734 a new campaign opened in the *Gentleman's Magazine*—the same magazine for which Dr. Johnson had an affection and for which he wrote the Parliamentary comment under the title of *The Senate of Lilliput* in pre-Hansard days. In its issue of January[1] a letter to the editor, ostensibly written with the editorial pretence of the period by a relative, was printed. I quote it here almost in full because it seems to me an entertaining as well as an informative comment on current calendar conditions:

To the Author of the Gentleman's Magazine

Gray's Inn, Jan. 1, 1734–5.

Dear Cousin,

I cannot enter upon the New Year, in which I wish you all the felicity you can desire, without troubling you with a few thoughts, which if you approve of, I should be glad if you would submit to the Public.

[1] Note date on following letter.

F

As History is my favourite amusement, and an exact Chronology is the surest guide to History, I find myself often perplexed with the notorious disagreement in Dates from Christmas to Lady-Day by almost every English Historian; and should therefore rejoice to see this uncertain Epoch (if it may be so called) reduced to a regular and certain Standard. This is the good wishes and Presents that are now circulated amongst Mankind, by the Director of the Almanacks, and by the concurrence of most chronological tables: And though I am no Pretender to Etymologies, I am far from thinking it an improbable conjecture that *January* has its Name from *Janua*, because 'tis a Gate which opens into the year: Nevertheless, how is the World confounded, not so much by the Difference between the old and new Stile founded on the *Julian* and *Gregorian* Epochas, as by the Briefs of the Pope's, which, Mr. Rapin observes, begin the year on the 25th of *December*, and by those of our Lawyers, who make it begin upon the 25th of *March*, and if I may use the expression, turn the Gate of the year into its Back-door!

The monstrous Absurdity of such a Variety of Dates is too notorious to every judicious Reader to be denied, and it is well observed by the Compiler of a late curious and seemingly exact Performance in the *Chronological* way, that it must eternally be productive of gross anachronisms, if the Differences be not very carefully attended to. That Author, after having remarked in his Preface to a *daily* Chronicle and *yearly* Journal, called the REMEMBRANCER, what errors are owing to the difference of the old and new stile, and to the computation of the year from the 25th of *March*, gives two palpable instances of the comparison that attends such a disagreement in Dates. He refers his Readers but to the years backward, for three State Papers that were then published in one week with three different Denominations of the year of Our Lord, viz; His Majesty's Speech dated 1732–3: The Lords' Address 1734 and the Commons Address 1733. So that if a person meets with those Addresses some years hence, he may well incline to think they were printed in different years, unless he happens to have before him at the same time, that very speech from the Throne to which they are Answers.

The other instance given in the *Remembrancer's* Preface is

the Epidemical Colds that then reigned in this part of the world, when some of our News-Papers were dated in 1732, and others in 1733, from whence he very justly concludes, that it will not be strange if, hereafter, People should be in some Doubt whether that Distemper happened in 1732 or 1733; And it will appear upon Retrospection that there has been the same Reason for the same Remarks in the Papers of former years, printed between *New Year's Day* and *Lady*-Day. In Order therefore to preserve an Uniformity so absolutely necessary in the Dates of History, the *Remembrancer* has been at the Pains to ascertain the Events to a greater Exactness of time than I have yet seen in any Chronology, by reducing the *new* Stile to the *old* in the Calculation of Days, and by conforming with all other Nations in beginning the Year on the *First of January*.

While I was ruminating on this subject, I could not help thinking that it would have contributed not a little to a clearer understanding of many Historical Passages, if all annual Elections to Offices, had been made upon the *First of January:* But this only by the way. I cannot conclude, however, without observing a Custom of some Booksellers who are apt to run the year forwards, so that I have seen Pamphlets published in *December*, and even in *November*, with the ensuing year ante-dated in the Title-Page; which Practice has been the Occasion of Perplexity to the curious Reader, when he has lain under a Necessity to consult some Books, particularly Lists of Parchment, etc.

These Observations, how trivial soever they may appear to some people at first sight, are in my humble Opinion, too material to be overlooked; but whether they are Right or Wrong, is submitted to Superiors, and if they think them worthy of their Animadversion I have my aim; History will have better Guides, and our News-Papers will no longer be liable to the Ridicule of being the only Papers in the World that have not any certain Dates to shew when they were published.

I will take up no more of you room than to subscribe myself

your loving Cousin,

URBANUS SYLVAN.

P.S. I observe that some of our Papers are now dated 1734, the very same date which they had this time Twelve Months, others are dated 1735, and some dated 1734–5. 'Tis humbly queried whether it would not be more proper that all Printers agreed to distinguish the doubtful Part of the Year by the double Date of 1734–5.

For the next few years articles and letters about the calendar appeared in this and other periodicals of the time. Generally they were concerned with the anomalies of religious dates, centring mainly on Easter and the inconvenience of its instability in the calendar, as well as scholarly debates on the exact dates on which it should properly be celebrated. It was in reply to one such letter in the *Gentleman's Magazine* that there appeared one of the most remarkable contributions to the subject.

It took the form of a long letter from a reader in Maryland, then one of the American colonies. It was signed with a *nom de plume*, and the astonishing thing about it is that although it was written by a man who was obviously a scholar and a mathematician, as well as probably an astronomer of no little learning, its writer has not to this day been identified. In it Hirassa ap-Iccim, as he called himself, proposed reforms which, as far as the calendar is concerned, at any rate, are still the subject of controversy. His letter, however, was not confined entirely to the calendar, but went also into the defects, as they seemed to him, of our system of coinage and weights and measures. His letter included an 'Essay on the British computation of time, coins, weights and measures', of which the following is the part with which we are concerned:

'Tis self-evident that our division of quantities are irregular, troublesome in practice, and repugnant to the nature of things; but that they are reducible to a proper adjustment may appear (I presume) from what follows.

First, as to our *computation of time.*

Even the present commencement of our Aera is known to be erroneous, Christ being born 4 years before the date we refer to; for his nativity was in the 4710th year of the Julian period; whereas Dionysius Exiguus (who hath brought this Aera into use as late as the 6th century) thro' mistake placed it in the 4714th.

Then as to the commencement of our year, how absurd and unstable it is, never to begin at the beginning; and tho' we have two beginnings to the same thing, yet to have each of these shifting and varying? Certainly the sun (that grand regulator of time), ought to be regarded as the Index of our years; since they entirely depend on the annual revolutions.

Again as to the length of our years, 'tis notorious that neither the *Julian* or *Gregorian* keep equal pace with the sun; so that in the latter the months will revolve (though more slowly than in the former) quite round the circle of the seasons.

Next as to our months: how confusedly is the year divided into 12 kalendar months, some consisting of 30, some of 31, and February of 28, and sometimes 29 days!

Lastly as to our days: how preposterously the days of the week vary in different months of the same year, and again in the same months of different years!

Having thus set out the calendar's more conspicuous defects the writer went on to deal with them in detail one by one, and to bring his considerable astronomical and historical knowledge to bear on suggestions for correcting them:

To remedy this, suppose a new account of time was established (in perpetual memory of his majesty K. George, denominated the *Georgian* account) in some such manner as follows, viz:

1st, Suppose the 4 defective years were added to our date, so that the next year (for instance) was called 1750; since in reality 'tis not the 1746th,[1] but the 1750th from the birth of Christ, at which remarkable point the Christian aera is intended to commence.

[1]The letter was written in 1745.

2ndly, Would we set out with the Sun ? Let us recede to the 11th of December, and make that the 1st day of our new year, when the sun begins his return from his winter solstice, at which *tropical* point Cæsar intended to fix the 1st of Jan.

3rdly, Would we keep pace with the sun in the length of our years? Let every 4th year (except the 132nd) consist of 366 days, as it does at present. But then forasmuch as the tropical year (according to Sir Isaac Newton) consists of 365 D 5 H 48' 57" (not of 365 D 6 H, the supposed length of the Julian year) therefore we annually overrun the sun 11' and 3" (or 44' 12" in every leap year) which in 132 years amounts of a day, wanting by 18' 36". But this small deficiency will not make an alteration of a natural day in *ten thousand years*; Therefore suppose that every 132nd (or 33d leap) year was to consist of but 365 days, like the common years: Thus would the civil year keep pace with the solar; so as not to vary a whole Nucthemeron in the long period of 10,000 years; And when the difference mounts to a whole natural day, allowance may be made for it to endless generations, as long as time itself shall last, or the sun and the earth endure in the positions and motions they have at present.

4thly, As to our months. Since the common year contains 365 days, or 52 weeks with an odd day; is it not naturally divisible into 13 months, each consisting of 28 days or 4 weeks? And might not the supernumerary day be properly (as it were) sequestered by Christians out of the year, and appropriated (between the end of the old and the beginning of the new year) to the celebration of the nativity of our blessed Saviour ? As to the names of the 13 months, the Quaker method of numbering them (*fas est et ab haste doceri*) I think would be the most proper; not indeed out of any conscientious scruple about the present names; but only because by numbering them thus would exhibit at once a clear idea of the part of the year in which we at any instant are, or wherein any occurrences happen, any transactions are registered, or any appointments are assigned. But, if the present names must be retained, may not the 13th month be called *Georgy*, in honour of K. George, as well as July was denominated for Julius, and August for Augustus Cæsar ?

5thly, As to the days of the week: they might either be

called by their number (after the same manner and for the same reasons as the months) or retain their present names, if the other preferable method be rejected: Then there would be this great advantage, that the days of every week would fall out perpetually on the same respective days of each month. The 1st, 8th, 15th and 22nd days might be the stated Christian Sabbaths or Sundays, and the other days of the week would regularly be fixt in every month in every year; and each of our 13 fixt holy-days might then be located to a certain day of every month, as set stages in our annual course of life.

Then this learned correspondent, whom no contemporary convention of time-counting daunted, tackled that most controversial problem of all—the propensity of Easter to wander with the moon. He actually proposed a 'fixed' Easter.

And whereas our moveable fasts and festivals depend on Easterday (which shifts irregularly for the compass of 35 days from March 22 to April 25) suppose Easter was fixt on the Sunday nearest to that day, on which the sun comes to the very same degree in the ecliptic, where it was on the day of the resurrection, which might easily be calculated. Then might all the other (now moveable) days be fixt at their proper distances from Easter; except the academical and Westminster term days, assizes, etc., which (in my humble opinion for the benefit of all parties concerned) ought to be fixt to certain proper seasons at due stated distances.

As to the 366th day in every 4th year (except the 132d before rejected) might it not be intercalated between the new and the old years after Christmas Day, and be set apart for solemn prayers for the prosperity of our king and countries, and be called the *British Lustrum*, *Olympiad*, or the *National Day*?

Thus were the Georgian account established by proper authority, our calculation of time would be correct, rational and easy: For our christian date would commence exactly with the birth of Christ: Our year would commence and keep pace with the sun: Our months would be regularly divided into weeks: and our days commodiously fixt, and methodically appropriated, some for religion, and the rest for wordly business; and all this for periods of endless generations.

A remarkable letter, a truly remarkable letter, considering its date. It must be remembered that this was written and printed seven years before the adoption in England of the Gregorian calendar. It is undoubtedly the first recorded suggestion of a perpetual calendar, a calendar which would align the weeks in a regular pattern with the years. It was to be nearly ninety years before the 'perpetual' idea was mooted again, and over a hundred before the 13-month solution which Hirassa ap-Iccim suggested was again put forward as a practical proposition. The strange thing is that so little note seems to have been taken of it. No controversy burst out in the *Gentleman's Magazine*, as might reasonably have been expected, and as certainly would have happened to-day had it been published, in like circumstances, in *The Times*. Not even the Earl of Macclesfield, who was probably the most knowledgeable of men of the period in calendar science, appears to have noted it, although one can assume that he must have known of it, if not personally have read it, for there is no reference, direct or indirect, to such a reform in his great disquisition to the House of Lords when, in February 1751, he put before the peers the case for the adoption of the Gregorian adjustment.

What did happen was that immediately after that speech, attention was suddenly focussed on Hirassa's ideas again when the *Gentleman's Magazine* in the following month, the March issue of 1751, published an appeal to its correspondent to write again, and added after referring to the letter printed in 1745: 'It is wished that a public demand had then been made for the author to send over his whole scheme; if he'll do us that favour, we'll endeavour to publish, or make some proper use of it'. But it was too late. In any case, the anonymous

Maryland genius appears never to have written again; perhaps, in the seven years that had passed between his first letter and the appeal, he had changed his mind about re-proposing a 'Georgian' era. Troubles between England and her American colonies were mounting, and America's War of Independence was on the way.

So the historic opportunity for the inauguration of a perpetual calendar was allowed to pass—and the world still waits for it.

PART TWO

CHAPTER I

Some Good (And Not So Good) Ideas

OPENING AT ITS first page the 1926 report of the League of Nations enquiry into calendar reform one reads that 'in recent times there have been a great number of international movements in favour of the reform of the present calendar', and it lists a few of them:

> In 1900, the Evangelical Conference at Eisenach;
> In 1910, the London Congress of the Permanent International Committee of the Chambers of Commerce and of Commercial and Industrial Associations;
> In 1914, the Paris Conference of the same associations;
> In 1914 also, the Liege Industrial Exchange;
> In 1919, the Congress of the International Astronomical Union which formed a special committee, of which the first President was the late Cardinal Mercier;
> In 1921, the London Conference of the International Chambers of Commerce; and
> In 1922, the Congress of the International Astronomical Union at Rome.

The list seemed to suggest that the idea was almost a newcomer among reform campaigns, a mere quarter of a century old at the time. In fact, it is a bearded old man among reformatory movements. It has been alive and more or less vigorous for two centuries and more.

Aside from the general perturbation that went on for hundreds of years and culminated in the continental Gregorian reform and, later, its adoption by the British

Parliament, the earliest recorded scheme for a wholesale overhaul of the calendar was contained in the mysterious Maryland letter. But when this received its evanescent publicity there still existed that incongruous diversity between the English and the continental calendars. A few years later it was corrected, and the Maryland letter, whose author in any case had not responded to the effort to identify him, was forgotten.

The beginning of the modern movement for reform is generally attributed to an Italian priest, the Abbe Mastrofini, who, in his book, *Amplissimi frutti da raccogliersi sul calendario gregoriano perpetuo*, published in Rome in 1834, proposed the following innovations in the Gregorian calendar:[1]

1. A year of 364 days instead of the usual 365 days, beginning on Sunday, January 1.
2. The three hundred sixty-fifth day in common years, allocated as an extra-calendrical day, to be called *feria Octava*, pending the approval of the Church.
3. The leap-year day either to follow the Gregorian practice, or to be placed after the *feria Octava* and to be called the *intercalary day*.

Mastrofini, however, proposed no changes regarding the irregularities of the months.

It would seem at first sight remarkable that this first accredited step towards revision of the existing calendar should have come from such a source, particularly in view of the totally reserved attitude of the Vatican in regard to the campaign for reform over the last thirty years. But it is not perhaps so astonishing when one considers the historical connections between the Church and the calendar. It was the Roman Catholic Church that brought about the Gregorian revision, and so cor-

[1] Bhola D. Panth, *Consider the Calendar* (Columbia University Press 1944).

rected the drift in the Julian system. It is an interesting fact also that among the proposals submitted to the League of Nations Calendar Committee, when that body invited ideas, were several from Roman Catholic clerics.

Of the Mastrofini plan, however, little further notice seems to have been taken, although Miss Achelis remarks that 'it received three *Nihil Obstats* and two *Imprimaturs* from his bishop'.[1]

Between the Maryland essay and the Mastrofini proposition however, there had occurred an event in calendar history that might well have ranked with Julius Cæsar's audacious action had not the political situation which gave it birth proved so much less permanent than that in which the Julian Calendar was born. That was the French Revolutionary Calendar, an attempt to take advantage of the great national upheaval in France to bring the latest scientific knowledge and practical experience to bear on this difficult subject. It attempted, once and for all, to dismiss convention and religion from the calendar, and to adapt it soundly and scientifically to convenience, bringing it at the same time into line with current methods of calculation.

It failed partly because it did not go far enough. It also came under severe reactionary pressure that was too powerful for it to withstand. But perhaps the strongest reason which led to its ultimate abandonment was its anti-Christian character, in the sense that it abandoned regard for the religious weeks.

The new revolutionary calendar was designed to mark a new era—the revolutionary or republican era. It was to do away entirely with the old system of time reckoning and the old nomenclature. The months were to be smoothed and equalized, and the week of seven days eliminated as a unit. The influence of the Church with

[1] Elisabeth Achelis, *The Calendar for Everybody* (Putnam, New York, 1943).

its saint's days and ecclesiastical fasts and feasts was to be completely expunged. The new calendar was to be scientific, practical, rational and convenient.

From the scientific point of view, the devising of the calendar was placed in the hands of the great French astronomer, Pierre Simon Laplace, and two eminent mathematicians Gaspard Monge and Joseph Louis Lagrange, the latter of whom seemed to be peculiarly qualified since he had earlier won a French Academy of Sciences prize for a Theory of the Libration of the Moon. To deal with the social implications, the dramatic poet Fabre d'Eglantine, then at the height of his fame with his new drama *L'Apothecaire*, was engaged. At the head of this distinguished committee was Charles Gilbert Romme, himself a mathematician, a member of the Convention, and president of the Committee of Public Instruction.

The committee was concerned to establish a correct 'start' for time, or at least for the new era, a more accurate system of keeping leap years in step than is the case with the Gregorian calendar, and a more rational system of division of the year and the day.

For the beginning of the count they argued—as astronomers have held since Sosigenes—that the obvious reasonable start of the year should be either at one of the solstices, or at one of the equinoxes. Since the start of the Republic practically coincided with the autumnal equinox—it was proclaimed by the Convention at its first sitting on September 21 1792—the point of midnight by Paris Observatory, September 21/22 was adopted as zero hour in the new time.

From this point the years were to be enumerated by Roman figures, as Anno I, Anno II, etc., a period of four years being termed a *Franciade*. The ordinary year was to consist of twelve months of 30 days, with five complementary days which were to be celebrated as holidays, and were dedicated (this was of course, like the remaining nomenclature, the work of d'Eglantine) to Virtue, Genius, Labour, Opinion and Rewards. The fourth, or leap year (rather misleadingly named the Sextile year) had an additional complementary day which was called Revolution Day, and dedicated to the revolution. The complementary days were to be known as *sans-culottes*, and dedicated to the poor.

But it was in the division of the day that the most startling changes were introduced. Here for the first time society was introduced to a practical decimal system, and it is apt to comment that it was all of a part with the scientific deliberations concerned with this calendar that the metric system—one of the greatest boons conferred by science on mankind—was evolved and shortly afterwards introduced. The month of 30 days was first divided into three periods of ten days each, called a *decade*. The day was then divided into ten hours (each hour equal obviously to 2·4 ordinary hours or 144 minutes). Each of the new hours however was freshly divided into 100 new minutes, and each of those minutes into 100 new seconds. It is regrettable to record that the decimal idea proved too confusing to the general public and was soon abandoned. Says Dr. Panth: 'Clocks with new dials were ordered to conform to the new decimal way of marking hours, minutes and seconds. However, because the suddenness of the new arrangement baffled the people, the subdivisions of the day were put off for a time, and eventually given up in 1795. Again, we see how the logic of science fell a victim to the established habits of society'.

The new months had new names, each expressing an attribute of its own character. Starting with the first month on the first day of the new period (September 22) the autumn months ran: Vendemaire, Brumaire and Frimaire (Vintage, Fog, and Frost); then the winter; Nivose, Pluviose and Ventose (Snow, Rain and Wind); spring: Germinal, Floreal and Prairial (Seed, Flower and Pasture); and finally summer: Messidor, Thermidor and Fructidor (Harvest, Heat and Fruit).

An elaborate system was evolved for correcting the slight Gregorian error of the centurial leap-years, but it had no chance to show its usefulness in practice, for 'despite his seeming preference for the Revolutionary Calendar, Napoleon used it as a bargaining wedge for a Concordat with the Pope. He obtained the Pope's formal recognition of his personal authority over France and parts of conquered Europe, and, as a price, abolished the Revolutionary Calendar and re-introduced the Gregorian Calendar, with its saints' days and church holidays, beginning with January 1 1806.'[1]

Still, it had lasted thirteen years, and however one regards it now, it was a great experiment.

Historians of the French Revolution have necessarily found the calendar system a difficulty, but various tables have been devised to adjust the chronology to Gregorian dates. The following, 'drawn up by Carlyle, enables one to transpose into the ordinary styles dates given in the style of the Revolution'.

To the number of days in	Add	We have the number of days in	Days
Vendemiaire	21	September	20
Brumaire	21	October	31
Frimaire	20	November	30
Nivose	20	December	31
Pluviose	19	January	31
Ventose	18	February	28
Germinal	20	March	31
Floreal	19	April	30
Prairial	19	May	31
Messidor	18	June	30
Thermidor	18	July	31
Fructidor	17	August	31

[1] B. D. Panth, *Consider the Calendar*.

'There are five Sansculottides, and in leap year a sixth, to be added at the end of Fructidor.'[1]

It was from France also that the next two important ideas concerned with the reform of the calendar came.

First of these was the evolutionary scheme devised by the philosopher Auguste Comte.

Comte, who founded the cult of Positivism, sought to embody in the calendar a synthesis of the evolution of humanity. He produced again the 13-month plan of dividing the year, and is recognized as the first of the modern proponents of this system. He returned to the 364-day year as a basis for making the calendar perpetual, proposing that the 365th and 366th should be extra-calendrical stabilizing days, so that his years would begin invariably on the same day of the week. That was, in his case, to be Monday, the day following the weekly day of rest. The year would always, therefore, begin on Monday, January 1. Each month would have exactly 28 days.

The most extraordinary feature of Comte's Positivist calendar, however, was its nomenclature. He did not merely add a newly-named month to the old, but re-christened them all, with names designed to perpetuate the memory of those whom he considered the world's greatest men: Moses, Homer, Aristotle, Archimedes, Cæsar, St. Paul, Charlemagne, Dante, Gutenberg, Shakespeare, Descartes, Frederick II and Bichat, in that order. The 52 weeks also had special and individual names, ranging through history. They included Numa, Buddha, Socrates, Confucius, Mohammed, from earlier days; Galileo, Bacon, Watt and Newton from more modern times. His days were to be called by still further names; every day a separate personality to give character and individuality to the day. The total number of names in the calendar was 559, and they covered the sweep of history from 3,200 years ago.

[1] H. Packwood Adams, *The French Revolution* (Methuen).

Elisabeth Achelis, who founded the World Calendar Association International, and has devoted her life and fortune to the cause of calendar reform.

SO NEAR AND YET SO FAR—The 1949 Agenda Committee of the U.N. General Assembly in Session. A General Committee of delegates of fourteen nations is elected by the Council whose duty it is to control the agenda and course of action of the General Assembly. This steering committee of 1949, by a tie vote of 4 to 4 (four abstaining; two absent) postponed action on the World Calendar at this session. Seated at the table (from left to right) are the delegates of Greece, France, Denmark, China, Chile, Canada, Brazil, (U.N. Secretary-General), Philippines. (Executive Assistant to the Secretary-General), Venezuela, United

Whether such nomenclature could ever have become popular can only be guessed; it has of course a pattern in the Saints' days of the church, but no doubt the numbers of the days would have continued in general use. The numbers made a simple monthly pattern:

Mon.	Tues.	Wed.	Thurs.	Frid.	Sat.	Sun.
1	2	3	4	5	6	7
8	9	10	11	12	13	14
15	16	17	18	19	20	21
22	23	24	25	26	27	28

It was the first time the exact, repeating 28-day month had been promulgated, and no doubt it had its appeal. At any rate, it was to be revived half a century later, stripped of its alleged philosophical significance, by Moses B. Cotsworth, a Yorkshire-born Canadian accountant, and to receive a great deal of attention in many countries.

There followed now a considerable interval before any outstanding new contribution was made to the reform controversy. It came in 1884, when the Astronomical Society of France, to promote interest in the subject, offered a number of prizes for the best plans for an improved calendar.

The first prize was won by a French astronomer, Gustav Armelin, who put forward a highly practical scheme for a time system based on the Gregorian calendar, departing very little from it except in month-end adjustments, and yet providing the desirable characteristics of perpetuity and easy divisibility into comparable periods of three and six months.

He adopted, to begin with, the principle of removing one day from the calendar proper, so that he was left with 364 days, or 52 weeks. (In leap years of course two days have to be so removed.) This was no novelty, but where he went further than his predecessors had done was in grouping the 52 weeks into exact quarters of 13

G

weeks, each quarter thus having 91 days. And leaving established custom still further, he readjusted the lengths of the months within the quarters so that they formed a repetitive series. Thus, the first month in the quarter would have 31 days, and the remaining two would each have 30. Total, 91.

He had achieved the 12-month, equal-quarter calendar.

The problem, however, does not finish here. Admitting that the general structure of such a calendar is probably the best ever likely to be achieved so long as seven-days weeks have to be fitted into both months and years, there are still difficult details to be decided. At what point in the year shall the calendar begin? Where shall the extra day—and in leap years, two days—be placed? What is the best day for the start of the week?

Armelin provided his own answers to these questions. The first day of the year he proposed to call January 0, which, occupying one of the 365, would leave 364 for the calendar proper, which would then begin nominally with the usual January 1. From then to the end of the year (in an ordinary year) the months would follow in regular sequence. January would have its usual 31 days, but February would have 30, and March again 30—first quarter; then April, 31, May, 30, June, 30—second quarter; and so on, each quarter having 91 days. When leap year came round, a day would be added to December, restoring it to its old length of 31 days instead of the 30 which it would otherwise get, and, unfortunately, breaking the sequence, once in four years, of the 91-day quarters. He proposed that his January 1 should be a Monday, from which it would follow that every year, and every quarter, and of course every half-year would always begin on Monday, ending on Sunday. At the end of the year there would be the stabilizing day, the *non dies*, falling between Sunday and Monday, the January 0, linking the old year to the new.

It could have been a very successful calendar, but there existed no machinery to put it into force. It was next heard of some forty years later—as File No. 35811 under Group B of the League of Nations' Classification and Summary of Proposals for Calendar Reform.

CHAPTER II

More Ideas—The Problem in Committee

BY FAR THE most important period in the history of
the calendar reform movement was that dating from
1923 and lasting into 1937, when it had reached the
widest international consideration and was in the hands
of the League of Nations. The two centuries of schemes
which form our theme might in fact be fairly neatly
divided into three parts—(1) pre-League; (2) League
study and activities; and (3) post-League. The first
section we have already tried to summarize: the third,
which overlaps a little into (2) is largely the story of
the American reformer, Elisabeth Achelis, and the
World Calendar Association, and her gallant fight for
reform in face of much discouragement; the second is the
record of the vast sorting out and shaking down of an
astonishing medley and confusion of ideas which was
performed by the League.

After the long series of resolutions by international
congresses which between 1900 and 1920 expressed
themselves in favour at least of studying the matter, it
was the formal demands uttered closely upon each other
by the International Chamber of Commerce and the
International Astronomical Union which at last raised
the subject to the level of supranational importance, and
compelled the newly founded League of Nations to
bring it within their review of outstanding world
problems.

The result was that (in the formal words of its 1926
Report) 'the Advisory and Technical Committee for
Communications and Transit, considering that the

investigation of the reforms which might be introduced into the Gregorian calendar would inevitably affect very considerably the conditions of economic life and international traffic by introducing a more uniform and more rational measurement of time, decided, at its fifth session, held at Geneva from August 29 to September 1, 1923, to set up a special Committee of Enquiry to go carefully into the question'.

But who was to be appointed to the decided-on Committee? Here was a most important facet of the problem. Before we discuss how it was answered, we should glance at the considerations which had moved these influential bodies, commercial and astronomical, whose deliberations had given rise to the League's decision to take steps in the matter at all.

The attitude of the International Chamber of Commerce, then itself a newly-formed body holding its first Congress in London in 1921, can be put in the few words contained in its Resolution dealing with the subject. It said briefly: 'The Congress of the International Chamber of Commerce approves the principle adopted by the Preliminary Committee for the Reform of the Calendar, that is to say, the principle of convening in the near future a special Congress at which the ecclesiastical, scientific and commercial world should be represented for the purpose of adopting a perpetual and fixed calendar'.

The International Astronomers went to very much greater length. The Minutes of their session in Rome in May, 1922, run to many pages and cover the various aspects of the subject under nine general headings:

1. Should a Calendar already in use but capable of improvement be taken as a basis?

2. Defects of the Gregorian Calendar.

3. Choice of the elements of the New Calendar: The Era. . . .

4. Length of the Year: Should the Gregorian Cycle of 400 Years be retained or altered ?
5. The Moment at which the Year should begin.
6. Divisions of the Year to be retained or established: Hours, Days, Weeks, Ten-day Periods.
7. If the Week is to be retained, should its Absolute Continuity also be adhered to ?
8. Months. Should there be twelve or thirteen months in the Year? How should they be named?
9. Festival of Easter.

In this way the astronomers divided up their debate into its essential sections, and there were learned disquisitions about each with a vote following on those sections that called for decision. By the end of the Conference they had come to four firm conclusions. One of these was contained in the report that 'The Committee expresses its desire that the festival of Easter should be stabilized'. The others, concerning the general calendar problem were, in the words of its Chairman, M. Bigourdan, 'summarized in the three following fundamental points':

1. Adoption of a perpetual calendar, keeping 52 weeks plus one or two blank days.
2. January 1 to take the place of the day at present occupied by December 22.
3. The 364 days to be divided into four periods of 91 days each, i.e., two months of 30 days and one of 31, without excluding an auxiliary division into periods of 14 and 28 days.

Thus there was no doubt of the direction in which scientific thought was moving, and the commercial world had been proclaiming the need for a less inconsistent calendar since 1910. There remained the religious point of view, which undoubtedly had to be considered. The fact that the question of the stabilization of Easter invariably arose even in secular discussions of the calendar was alone enough to accentuate the importance of this side of the argument. Moreover, almost all calendars (with the outstanding exception of the Julian) have been formed on the basis of religious observances, and even Julius Cæsar's system had become subservient to religious needs when Pope Gregory XIII re-adjusted it in 1582. The League, in appointing its Calendar Reform Committee, therefore decided to include not only representatives of the scientific and industrial worlds, but also members who should be competent to speak for the great religions. Accordingly three of the six members finally appointed were selected directly by and represented the Holy See, the Oecumenical Patriarch of Constantinople, and the Archbishop of Canterbury. They were respectively the Rev. Father Gianfrancheschi, President of the Academy *Die nuovi Lincei*; Professor D. Eginitis, Director of the Observatory of Athens and the Rev. T. E. R. Phillips, Secretary of the Royal Astronomical Society of London. That all were eminent in the astronomical field of learning is a salient fact, but in considering the progress made towards the universal adoption of a reformed calendar, and the strength of the demand for reform which emerged, it is most important to keep in mind that the religious side was never over-looked, but that the Committee had on the contrary an overwhelming bias in favour of its consideration. This point seems never to have been sufficiently emphasized.

For the rest, the Advisory and Technical Committee of the League nominated Jonkheer W. J. M. van Eysinga, a Professor at the University of Leyden, as chairman: M. G. Bigourdan, who had already studied the subject as chairman of the calendar reform committee of the International Astronomical Union; and finally, to represent industry, Mr. Willis H. Booth, President of the International Chamber of Commerce. It cannot he said that the commercial world, which in its vast complexity of day-to-day home and international affairs, so badly needs this reform, and in which its benefit would first and most continuously be felt, had anything like its fair representation. Much progress was made, it is true, but the business world still awaits a new calendar.

From Algeria to Uruguay, and from Chile to China and elsewhere—in all from thirty-three countries—the League of Nations received individual schemes for a revision, if not always a reform, of the calendar.

The invitation to make suggestions and submit ideas was one of the earliest actions of the League Committee when it set out to investigate the subject. Proposals came from far and wide. Up to the time of publication of its first Report in 1926 the total number was 185[1] and 'consideration was also given to a number of schemes already known to the Committee'.

To those who have not given the matter much attention, this figure must be surprising. At least it indicates the arbitrary nature of calendars in general, but it will perhaps not be so astonishing when one recalls that today in India alone more than thirty different calendars are in use simultaneously, and we have seen in earlier chapters how different nations devised entirely different systems of time-keeping for their national use.

Still, a day is a day, and a season a season. All calendrical devices must be based on these immutable facts. It would seem, therefore, that there is a limit to the possibilities. And so it turns out, for the Committee duly reported that 'after examining the last hundred received, although each had been conceived by its

[1] The quoted number of these schemes varies widely according to different authors. The figure given in the 1926 Report is 185, but in the analysis of schemes published in the following year only 152 submissions were dealt with, although in some cases one individual or organization had submitted alternative ideas. Proposals, however, continued to be received long afterwards, and the total has been variously mentioned as 'nearly 500', 'over 400' and similar figures, but it must be assumed that many were merely duplicates.

author on an original basis, none offered any new combination that could reasonably be put into practice . . . and all combinations which can be carried out with any hope of success are known to the Committee'.

It seemed a reasonable conclusion, for the book which simply summarized the proposals, giving half a dozen lines or so to each, contains 58 pages, most of them devoted to these swift precis. They divided the plans first into a number of main groups, such as Perpetual Calendars, Non-perpetual, projects dealing only with leap-years, others only with the stabilization of Easter, and 'others'.

First came the group whose sponsors favoured the thirteen-months calendar, and this was at the time the largest group of all, for it was the period when Mr. Cotsworth was actively recommending the adoption of this plan, and the International Fixed Calendar League, which advocated it, was still in existence, and working hard in its cause. Because of this the Cotsworth proposal received more space than any other single scheme in the report, and since it provides the basis on which no doubt many others had been built, the summary is worth consideration. It was headed 'Proposer's name: Moses B. Cotsworth, and International Fixed Calendar League; Year of Proposal: 1895', and set out the basis of the plan in eleven points:

1. 13 months of 28 days.
2. The 13th month, 'Sol,' to be inserted between June and July.
3. The year to begin on January 1.
4. The first day of the year to be a Sunday or Monday.
5. The annual blank day to be on December 29 of reformed calendar;
6. Leap-day to be on June 29 of reformed calendar (June 18 of the Gregorian calendar).
7. Easter to be on April 15 of reformed calendar (April 9 of the Gregorian calendar).

8. Months ought to be indicated by Roman numerals, not by names. If names are necessary, it is proposed that the twelve Zodiacal names be used, with 'Sol' as the inserted month.

9. It would be preferable to continue the Gregorian adjustments for leap years to 2,000 which would be a *non*-leap year, but every 128th year following omit leap-day, to keep the calendar truest to solar time for all future years.

10. The days of the week to be internationally indicated by quarter-moon signs.

11. The 24-hour system of daily time to be internationally established.

Reading through these points, one cannot fail to be struck by the obvious thoroughness with which Mr. Cotsworth had studied his subject. It is true that it had been in his mind for a very long time; 1895, the date given as its origin, gave the plan thirty years of seniority over most of the novel schemes which the League had now to consider, and he had consequently had all this time to devote to the details. It is the details which are, in fact, surprising, for the thirteen-month principle itself was by no means new even in 1895. As we have seen, it had been the basis of the Auguste Comte plan in 1849, and before that (although it had no official recognition, and has none now), it had been mooted by the mysterious Maryland correspondent of the *Gentleman's Magazine* a hundred years earlier. Cotsworth carries it much further. He embodies in his proposals—at least as they were submitted to the League Committee—elaborations which at best can only be regarded as embellishments of no major importance to its structure.

That he should have concerned himself with such details for example as the writing of the months in Roman numerals, thus 28.VI.53, and, still more remarkable, with calling them by Zodiacal names could but confuse the main issue. The Zodiac idea was surely a retrograde step, for, apart from the fact that the Zodiac periods are slowly changing in their relations to the months, it smacks rather of astrology than the astronomy on which a scientific calendar must necessarily be based. His 'quarter-moon signs' for the days of the week, too, are vaguely suggestive of *Old Moore's Almanack*, and his 24-hour day, while sensible in itself and an obviously reasonable improvement, had already been tried out in various places and found to be unpopular in general application.

What is evident, however, is the wholly estimable desire to internationalize the calendar. In recommending his zodiacal and quarter-moon devices he was at least providing a nomenclature which was, if not fully under-stood by everyone, at least not unfamiliar, and, since it was already roughly known, was capable of being easily adopted.

That this question of the names of the months had some right to consideration is indicated by the remark-able difference of opinion, not to say inventiveness, which was shown in the suggestions for the name of the thirteenth month which were made by the various pro-posers of this kind of scheme. Cotsworth has called his, 'Sol', but here are some of the alternatives which the League had put before it for consideration:

Floréal	Undezember	Floral
Minerva	Medial	Treizier
Salvator	Christ	Maxime
Luno	Liberty	Benedict or Pius
Vincent	Venus	Evember
Trecember	Moses	Mois de l'année
Lunes	Vacance	Advent
Sextember		

As to where this thirteenth month might best be placed was also a matter of differing opinion. Cotsworth proposed to place it plumb in the centre of the year, between June and July, where no doubt he felt it would have the least unbalancing effect on the calendar as a whole. Even then, however, and this is one of the major drawbacks of the thirteen-month scheme, it would have the effect of making comparisons with the present calendar extremely difficult. The disparity would begin to be apparent from February 1, which would be the 29th day of the year, and require enumeration of weeks and months entirely different than those current to the time of its adoption. While the end of June would be 'minus' fourteen days the beginning of July would represent a plus figure of fourteen and these differences would continue throughout. (One of the most attractive features of the proposed World Calendar is that it achieves regularity without at any time varying more than two days in sequence from a similar date in the Gregorian calendar).

However, there were plans which sought to minimize this problem, as in the Victor Stall method, which proposed to put the new month after December; while others, like the Juan Marinero system which would insert it between March and April and J. H. Nayman, an American, put it between April and May. M. Vincent-Arnould, of Belgium, placed it between February and March. Yet another, the Lensch plan, made it the first month of the new year. One rather remarkable suggestion came from Fritz Reininghaus, of Zurich, and proposed a year of twelve months of 28 days and two half-months of 14 days. Beginning his year with the 1st of Prim, which was to be a Monday, he proposed to name his months Prim, Secund, Terz, Quart, Quint, and Sect, followed by the 'Half Summer Month', and then Septum, Octav, Non, Decim, Undec, and Duodec, ending with the 'Half Winter Month'. After that would come the extra-calendrical day, and in leap years, also the leap year day.

Among other thirteen-month proposals—and out of the 152 of all the groups summarized, 36 fell into this category—there were many variations on the theme, some novel, but there was this one point which they are shared in common: the extra-calendrical, or, as the official documents rather badly term it, the 'blank' day principle. This principle is in fact indispensable in a perpetual calendar, and there would seem to be no purpose in the introduction of the smooth 28-day month system unless at the same time the dates in consecutive years are made to agree with week-days.

The International Posivitist Society put forward a project under the date 1913 which, commented the League Report, was 'identical with the plan proposed by Auguste Comte in 1849'.[1]

It was M. Paul Delaporte, who, on behalf of the Economica Chronos League, of Paris, in his proposal of what he described as a thirteen-month 'auxiliary' calendar, put forward a constructive idea for dealing with the extra-calendrical day. His year 'Chronos' was to begin on any date in the Christian year, but 'the annual blank day would form a supplementary day and be reckoned separately at the end of the year, *or could be accumulated until a supplementary week could be formed*'.

Here was what seems to have been the first suggestion of the 'leap-week', an idea of which much has since been heard and of which much will probably yet be heard when the subject of calendar reform comes—as it must come—before the United Nations Organization for ultimate decision, or at least for re-investigation. That extra-calendrical, or 'blank' day, as the opponents of calendar reform invariably term it, has been the main stumbling block which has held up progress. It is a curious fact that the Report comments immediately after this Delaporte suggestion that 'This as an auxiliary system does not seem directly to concern the calendar', but there is no doubt that it is one of the most important

[1] See page 88.

suggestions made. There are many of the opponents of reform whose opposition is based entirely on the necessity for a 'blank' day and its consequent disturbance of the sequence of weeks, who would be quite willing to withdraw such opposition if those annual extra-calendrical days were saved up to form, every five or six years, an extra week. In their view, that it would disregard astronomical facts and measurements is not so serious as that the World Calendar, for instance, would introduce once a year (and twice in leap years) an eight-day week.

Before discussing the many variants of the twelve-month calendar which formed the major section of the report, it will be interesting to look at some of the schemes that one is tempted to label as oddities. Designating them thus is not to say that, given a more familiar background, they might not provide quite sensible solutions of the calendar problem, but our conditioning through all our contacts with the subject to regarding the year as divisible only into months which at least has some correspondence with the moon and into weeks of seven days, tends to make us think of any widely differing plan—perhaps wrongly—as somewhat freakish. Such was the case with the decimal calendar of the French Revolution: Napoleon's dislike of it and its ultimate abandonment were probably due as much to the difficulty of 'getting used to it' as to any other reason.

So it would probably be again if some of these more extreme calendar schemes of the early 'twenties came into use. Take, for example, the Dr. H. Zeigler plan submitted to the League in 1924. This proposed a year of nine months, each of 40 days. Each month was to have five weeks of eight days, and to compensate for the extension of the accepted working week Dr. Ziegler indicated that there should be one additional day's holiday, or an extra half-holiday, in each eight-day period.

Since the nine 40-day months would total only 360 days in the year, he suggested that there should be five *non dies* at the end of the year (six of course in leap years), a proposal which has several precedents in calendar history, and is particularly reminiscent of the Aztecs and their 'unlucky' days. So far, however, the eight-day week has never been tried.

From Senor M. M. Vidal, of Spain came the suggestion of a ten-month year, divided into 36 'diacronos', standardizing the calendar on the 'cronos' as a unit of time, this cronos being the 100,000th part of the ratio of the ecliptic to the equivalent equatorial times.

The idea of a ten-month year came from a number of different people. Mr. Wladyslaw Zedzianowski, of Poland, proposed to have alternate months of 36 and 37 days (a total of 365) making his leap-year the 37th day of the tenth month. Beyond this he proposed a decimal division of the day into ten 'great hours'. Each great hour was again divided into 100 solar minutes and each minute into 100 solar seconds. An American, Mr. Edward Skille, of Drummond, Wis., had the same idea with regard to 36- and 37-day months, which he wished to call 'mona', but suggested the year's division into 73 five-day weeks (which he called 'metos') and he gave the names Ano, Beno, Ceno, Deno and Eno to the five days respectively. Again he planned a centisimal division of the day putting forward the idea of dividing it into 100 parts called Ceni, the Ceni into 100 smaller parts called Deni, and that in its turn into 100 still smaller parts to be known as Eni.

A particularly simple plan was that of Mr. Stijepo-Ferri of the then Kingdom of the Serbs, Croats and Slovenes whose design was to abolish months altogether and number the days consecutively, from 1 to 365 or 366. On the other hand, Mr. Jakob Uhlmann, of Vienna, wished to divide the year into 24 months. M. Peroslav Paskievie, an ex-Secretary-General of the Chamber of

Commerce at Zagreb, strongly pressed for the re-adoption of the French Revolutionary calendar *in toto*, but with a rest day only every tenth day. He commented: 'With an eight-hour working day, a rest-day every seventh day is too much'. A variation in the arrangement of months came from M. Peltekis, of Greece, whose idea was that, with a twelve-month calendar, the first six months should have 31 days, and the others 30 except the last which in ordinary years would get only 29, but 30 in leap years. He coupled this with the suggestion of a five-day week.

Another of the groups into which the League of Nations Committee had sorted out its welter of proposals was one which it classified as '53 weeks, and other proposals suggesting the elimination of the annual blank day and the leap day in order to maintain the continuity of the cycle of weeks of seven days'. This was Group E and some of the suggestions contained in it may yet come up for further debate, although the League was to come to the conclusion, before their deliberations ended, that only two—the Cotsworth thirteen-month and the World twelve-month, equal-quarters, calendars merited further consideration; and finally only one—the World Calendar—was a practical proposition.

However that may turn out, the group contained 14 different proposed systems, which to say the least are ingenious, as well as interesting. Baron Gustav Bedeus, of Rumania, proposed that the year should have twelve months, eight of them with 28 days and the other four with 35. He also had a complicated system of 'extra-ordinary' years and days. There was to be an 'extraordinary' year of 371 days (the last months having 35 days) every five or six years; and these were to occur, for 50 years every fifth year, and for 90 years, every sixth; but to keep in step one of these extraordinary years was to be omitted every 896th year. (This was probably the basis of the arrangement suggested by the Royal Statistical Society's Committee).[1]

Three alternative plans came from the Abbé Ed. David of the Petit Seminaire de Perpignan. Two of these were similar in their main content to the Delaporte plan which we have already considered, providing a leap week every fifth or sixth year instead of a leap day, thus avoiding the occurrence of an eight-day week while still achieving a perpetual calendar. His years were to begin on a Sunday, January 1, but the principal difference in these two alternatives—especially interesting as coming from a priest—were that in one of them he suggested that Easter should be on April 1, fixed, while in the other he proposed that it should be April 15, fixed.

His third plan struck a new note. In it he suggested that the 364 days of the year, divided into thirteen 28-day months, should be maintained until the extra-calendrical days and leap year days had amounted to a further 28, when he would have a leap month. This would occur every 22 or 23 years, and the Abbé proposed whenever it fell due, to insert it between January and February of the appropriate year, which would give that year 14 months, and a total of 78 weeks. His regular 13th month he suggested should be inserted between August and September each year.

A similar idea to that of the Abbé came from another Frenchman, M. Armand Lipman, of Versailles, who also planned a thirteen-month year with a fourteenth month occurring after 23 years. The remaining calendar-makers in the group plumped for the leap week every five or six years, with one variation, that of Lt.-Col. de Saint-Hillier, also of France, whose idea was to have five extraordinary years of 53 weeks coming together after every 28 years.

See page 177.

H

The suggestion of a six-day week occurs fairly frequently but the most unusual one is that of Josef von Erny, of Budapest, whose plan visualized a year of 20 months, of three weeks each, each week to have ordinarily only six days, i.e. omitting Saturdays, but in the 1st, 5th, 9th, 13th and 17th months one week would restore the Saturday and thus have seven days. His leap-day he proposed to insert after the 18th day of the 20th month in leap years.

Another group of schemes which came within the range of the League's consideration consisted of those which dealt with 'projects proposing modification of the Gregorian rule with regard to leap years', and though it was small in number, it required careful thought, for suggestions under this heading concerned periods of thousands of years at one extreme and fractions of seconds at the other. Yet another concerned exclusively the fixing of Easter, as that of Lord Desborough which led later to the passing of the ineffective Easter Act 1928; and a third the continuation of a non-perpetual calendar, which meant the present Gregorian with slight modifications made for convenience. Among these was the frequently quoted Alexander Philip suggestion to take August 31 and move it to the place of February 29— an apparently small adjustment which would nevertheless go far to equalize the quarters and half-years.

Having scanned the submissions that tended towards the revolutionary, we are on more familiar ground in examining those—and they formed a large group—which held to the twelve-months principle. There is a considerable sameness in general outline, though they differ widely in detail.

Without exception the authors give their months 30 and 31 days, with an occasional 29, and nowhere does the unbalanced February 28 of our Gregorian calendar appear. However, where the main difference arises is in the order in which the 30- and 31-day months occur—an extremely important point in considering the degree of convenience aimed at. We have seen already one case in which six months of 31 are followed by six of 30, with the last month reduced to 29 in other than leap years. There were others in which the 31 and 30 were planned to run alternately in regular sequence, with one exceptional month of one day less, except as before in leap years when the total can be brought up to 366 by keeping perfect regularity.

The main disadvantage of these proposals was that their authors sacrificed the equalization of the quarters, which most were unwilling to do. The majority of the arrangements therefore were based on the 91-day quarter of three months. The problem then reduced itself to how best to arrange the 30 and 31 figures in each quarter, with the subsidiary question of exactly when to start each quarter. In the case of perpetual calendars the day of the week on which the start of the year was made became tremendously important, for it affected the whole design of the calendar.

Obviously there had to be two thirties and a thirty-one in each quarter to make up the 91 days. Keeping the quarters the same in their total number of days the series could be set out in three different ways: 31, 30, 30; 30, 31, 30; or 30, 30, 31. It is around this order, closely connected with the question of the starting day of the week, that controversy still exists. Another possibility is that of varying the order, as did Mr. R. Baire, of Lausanne, who suggested the series 31, 30, 30—30, 31, 30—30, 31, 30—31, 30, 31, a sequence which adds up to 365 and includes as December 31 what in other cases is called the extra-calendrical day. His leap day he proposed to place as July 31, which would put both his 'extra' days into the second half-year, but he submitted also an alternative plan in which the leap year day would fall on June 31, thus equalising the half-years.

In the Baire case, the *shape* of the respective quarters would differ, and for greatest convenience this shape is important, in relation to the week. Since convenience is a major consideration—after all, the calendar is essentially a convenient way of counting the passing days—it is necessary to have the shape of the quarters in mind when the so-called equal-quarter calendars are concerned. In the following table are set out the three different arrangements of the 91-day quarter of three months, seen as beginning on a Sunday, compared with the same arrangements if the quarter begins on a Monday.

91-day quarter (31-30-30) with first month starting on Sunday

	January etc.	*February etc.*	*March etc.*
Sun.	1 8 15 22 29	5 12 19 26	3 10 17 24
Mon.	2 9 16 23 30	6 13 20 27	4 11 18 25
Tues.	3 10 17 24 31	7 14 21 28	5 12 19 26
Wed	4 11 18 25	1 8 15 22 29	6 13 20 27
Thurs.	5 12 19 26	2 9 16 23 30	7 14 21 28
Fri.	6 13 20 27	3 10 17 24	1 8 15 22 29
Sat.	7 14 21 28	4 11 18 25	2 9 16 23 30
	26 *week-days*	26 *week-days*	26 *week-days*

91-day quarter (31-30-30) with first month starting on Monday

	January etc.	*February etc.*	*March etc.*
Mon.	1 8 15 22 29	5 12 19 26	3 10 17 24
Tues.	2 9 16 23 30	6 13 20 27	4 11 18 25
Wed.	3 10 17 24 31	7 14 21 28	5 12 19 26
Thurs.	4 11 18 25	1 8 15 22 29	6 13 20 27
Fri.	5 12 19 26	2 9 16 23 30	7 14 21 28
Sat.	6 13 20 27	3 10 17 24	1 8 15 22 29
Sun.	7 14 21 28	4 11 18 25	2 9 16 23 30
	27 *week-days*	26 *week-days*	25 *week-days*

91-day quarter (30-31-30) with first month starting on Sunday

	January etc.	February etc.	March etc.
Sun.	1 8 15 22 29	6 13 20 27	3 10 17 24
Mon.	2 9 16 23 30	7 14 21 28	4 11 18 25
Tues.	3 10 17 24	1 8 15 22 29	5 12 19 26
Wed.	4 11 18 25	2 9 16 23 30	6 13 20 27
Thurs.	5 12 19 26	3 10 17 24 31	7 14 21 28
Fri.	6 13 20 27	4 11 18 25	1 8 15 22 29
Sat.	7 14 21 28	5 12 19 26	2 9 16 23 30
	25 week-days	27 week-days	26 week-days

91-day quarter (30-31-30) with first month starting on Monday

	January etc.	February etc.	March etc.
Mon.	1 8 15 22 29	6 13 20 27	3 10 17 24
Tues.	2 9 16 23 30	7 14 21 28	4 11 18 25
Wed.	3 10 17 24	1 8 15 22 29	5 12 19 26
Thurs.	4 11 18 25	2 9 16 23 30	6 13 20 27
Fri.	5 12 19 26	3 10 17 24 31	7 14 21 28
Sat.	6 13 20 27	4 11 18 25	1 8 15 22 29
Sun.	7 14 21 28	5 12 19 26	2 9 16 23 30
	26 week-days	27 week-days	25 week-days

91-day quarter (30-30-31) with first month starting on Sunday

	January etc.	February etc.	March etc.
Sun.	1 8 15 22 29	6 13 20 27	4 11 18 25
Mon.	2 9 16 23 30	7 14 21 28	5 12 19 26
Tues.	3 10 17 24	1 8 15 22 29	6 13 20 27
Wed.	4 11 18 25	2 9 16 23 30	7 14 21 28
Thurs.	5 12 19 26	3 10 17 24	1 8 15 22 29
Fri	6 13 20 27	4 11 18 25	2 9 16 23 30
Sat	7 14 21 28	5 12 19 26	3 10 17 24 31
	25 weekdays	26 week-days	27 week-days

91-day quarter (30-30-31) with first month starting on Monday

	January etc.	February etc.	March etc.
Mon.	1 8 15 22 29	6 13 20 27	4 11 18 25
Tues.	2 9 16 23 30	7 14 21 28	5 12 19 26
Wed.	3 10 17 24	1 8 15 22 29	6 13 20 27
Thurs.	4 11 18 25	2 9 16 23 30	7 14 21 28
Fri.	5 12 19 26	3 10 17 24	1 8 15 22 29
Sat.	6 13 20 27	4 11 18 25	2 9 16 23 30
Sun	7 14 21 28	5 12 19 26	3 10 17 24 31
	26 week-days	26 week-days	26 week-days

What is seen here is the difference in the number of week-days per month which result from the various arrangements, and herein lies the importance of the choice of the order of the 31 and the 30 within the boundary of the quarter. For modern industrial and commercial statistical purposes, where comparisons of working periods are concerned it is obvious that month-by-month records are tremendously facilitated if the number of working days in the months is always the same.

It cannot be said that at this point any marked preference was shown for one arrangement rather than the other, comparing the 31, 30, 30 with the 30, 30. 31 among the proposals which the League had to consider. Nor was the choice between a Sunday start for the year rather than a Monday as definite as might have been expected. There was also one suggestion for starting on a Friday, while several referred to the desirability of beginning the year with the winter solstice. (This question of the start of the year at one of the solstices or the equinoxes later developed into a major subject of debate, which is dealt with elsewhere in this book.)

Beyond these points there was on the whole nothing much to choose between the many submissions which fell into this general category of the equal-quarter perpetual calendar. There were differing ideas about positioning the extra-calendrical day and the leap day. The extra day in some cases was to be the 1st of the month, in others the 31st, while some suggested calling it January 0 or December 0 and leaving out a number entirely. One suggestion was that the leap day should fall between August 14 and 15 (without a date) and another that it should return to its true Roman bis-sextile place in the calendar and become again a second February 24. The Abbé Chauve-Bertrand suggested that Christmas should fall on 0 of the 1st month, and that this should also be the extra-calendrical day.

An interesting comment on one proposal was that Sunday, Saturday and Friday should be arranged to coincide for Christians, Jews and Mohammedans (although the report which makes the comment does not explain how this would be done), and there came a charming touch from the famous French astronomer, M. Camille Flammarion, who submitted as new names for the twelve months: Truth, Science, Wisdom, Justice, Honour, Kindness, Love, Beauty, Humanity, Happiness, Progress and Immortality.

CHAPTER III

Another Experiment

DURING THE VERY time when the distinguished committee of religious, scientific and commercial gentlemen were deliberating on calendar reform at Geneva; while they were actually studying the learned and ingenious proposals which had poured into their council from everywhere; and while they were preparing their later guarded recommendations, practical trials of reform were taking place in the U.S.S.R.

At the time of the revolution in Russia, that country was still using the old Julian calendar, as was the case with other nations where the Eastern Orthodox Church had greater influence than the Roman Catholic, but one of the first acts of the Soviet Government was to adopt the Gregorian system to bring its chronology into line with the rest of the world. By this time, the Julian calendar had drifted another two days since Pope Gregory's adjustment. To bring it up to date the Council of People's Commissars issued a decree on January 26 1918, dropping thirteen days from the Russian calendar. It is this thirteen days which explains the apparent anomaly of the celebration of the 'October Revolution' in November and similar historical situations.

That, however, was merely an overdue and inevitable revision. What was more remarkable was the experiment made in 1929 with a novel 'week' as a unit of working time. Instead of the seven-day week as a basis, it was decided to adopt a five-day period, severing the week completely from its religious associations and instituting a system of four days' work followed by one day's rest.

This rest day was, moreover, to be staggered so that factories and workshops would be operating continuously. How it worked is well described by two American investigators who made an intense study of Russian developments at the time.[1]

In October of that year (1929) every book-stall in Moscow and many newsboys displayed gaily coloured calendars for the year 1929–30. Each day of the new five-day week was given a colour. And each worker in a factory, office or store counted his day of rest by his assigned colour. The order, from first to fifth, was yellow, orange, red, purple and green. Five red stars indicated the national holidays: January 22nd, May 1st and 2nd, November 7th and 8th.

Soon after arose confusion. How was one to remember the free day of one's friends or business acquaintances? They very soon became yellow or green and were so listed in one's address book. Much discussion arose and confusion worse confounded. Should the days of the week be renamed for revolutionary heroes or slogans? Should the months be obliterated? But custom and especially foreign correspondence and trade eliminated these suggestions. In January the calendars were printed by number and not by colour, and each person noted his free day as the first day, or the second day, and so on, and each person was given a calendar showing his or her free day. One's address book now listed against each name the holidays by number instead of by colour. It was easy to remember ones and fives and sevens, or threes and eights. But the problem of the short month of February and the 31-day months remained. In some offices the 31st day of the month was taken either as a holiday, or as extra work according to the needs of the office. In industry it was always an extra work-day. Thus the first of each month was always the first of the week, and the calendars were so printed.

The social effects of this system seem to have been its undoing. Methods had to be devised to enable families to have coincident free days, facilities for recreation

[1] Susan M. Kingsbury and Mildred Fairchild in *Factory, Family and Woman in the Soviet Union* (Putnam, New York, 1935).

SOVIET FIVE-DAY WEEK CALENDAR, JANUARY–JUNE 1930

RED DAYS

Month	Mon	Sun	Sat	Fri	Thu	Wed	Tue	Mon	Sun	Sat	Fri	Thu	Wed	Tue	Mon	Sun	Sat	Fri	Thu	Wed	Tue	Mon	Sun	Sat	Fri	Thu	Wed	Tue	Mon	Sun	Sat	Fri	Thu	Wed	Tue
January		5	4	3	2	1		6	12	11	10	9	8	7	13	19	18	17	16	15	14	20	26	25	24	23	22	21	27			31	30	29	28
February		2	1					3	9	8	7	6	5	4	10	16	15	14	13	12	11	17	23	22	21	20	19	18	24			28	27	26	25
March	31	2	1					3	9	8	7	6	5	4	10	16	15	14	13	12	11	17	23	22	21	20	19	18	24	30	29	28	27	26	25
April		6	5	4	3	2	1	7	13	12	11	10	9	8	14	20	19	18	17	16	15	21	27	26	25	24	23	22	28					30	29
May		4	3	2	1			5	11	10	9	8	7	6	12	18	17	16	15	14	13	19	25	24	23	22	21	20	26		31	30	29	28	27
June	30	1						2	8	7	6	5	4	3	9	15	14	13	12	11	10	16	22	21	20	19	18	17	23	29	28	27	26	25	24

▥ Rest Days.   ▤ National Holidays.

This was one of the first series of five-day calendars; later the months were given 30 days each, plus the national holidays; and later again six-day weeks were adopted. Finally, these systems were abandoned and the seven-day week of the Gregorian calendar restored.

between friends and acquaintances were obviously affected, and although the experiment had a run of a year or two, it was then dropped in favour of a new idea— the six-day week.

This new plan came into use in 1932. It divided the year into twelve months, each month having five weeks of six days. The Gregorian month series, which had been dropped in favour of a 30-day system plus the national holidays, was restored, but the days of the week had no names, being numbered one to six and so on through the month. The Free Day, as the day of rest was termed, fell on the 6th, 12th, 18th, 24th and 30th in the ordinary way but in the case of February and the 31-day months adjustments were made. The last week in February either extended into a long week running to March 6, making a ten-day week (nine working days), or with the first week in March became one of two consecutive short weeks of five days (four working days). In the case of the 31-day months, the extra day was either tacked on to the working week or given as an extra day off, so that the following week would again start on the first of the month. In most schools and industries[1] before the war the day was spent in instructive games or was entirely devoted to military exercises.

'Elimination of the seven-day week and the practice of using numbers to indicate the day,' says B. D. Panth, 'removed the names of the week-days from common usage in urban areas. In rural areas, however, old social habits persisted and the ancient names of the seven days persisted. The total effect of the Soviet Union's calendar reforms, therefore, was that only the industrial population observed the six-day week, some special industries followed the five-day week, and the farmers, officials in the Foreign Office, and men and women who had to deal with foreign countries used the seven-day week. Otherwise, the calendar, as far as the months and number of

[1] B. D. Panth, *Consider the Calendar*.

days in the month were concerned, was identical with the Gregorian'.

Then came the war, which emphasized the difficulty of a single country carrying out calendar reforms in isolation. 'Recognizing the danger "towards the security and peace of their country in a world war," the All-Union Central Council of Trades Unions, as a measure of preparedness and vigilance, appealed to the Soviet Government to extend the working period. In compliance, the Presidium of Supreme Soviet in U.S.S.R. decreed the shift from a 60-week year based on a six-day week to the 52-week year based on a seven-day week. Since June 27 1940, the Soviet Union has again followed the Gregorian Calendar and, as a result, the seven-day week has been the rule for all state, co-operative, and social enterprises. This means that the day of rest is again officially observed once in seven days instead of once in six days or once in five days'.

What emerges from these abortive experiments with time seems to be that the exigiencies of modern industry combined with the habits that have grown up over centuries will successfully defeat any drastic and revolutionary changes in our calendar system at the present time, or certainly any changes which are not universally agreed before they are put into force.

CHAPTER IV

A Moslem Reform

A MOSLEM COUNTRY is perhaps where one would least expect to find a movement for calendar reform, for the Mohammedan calendar is tied so closely to the Mohammedan faith that the two would seem to be inseparable.

Before the time of the prophet Mahomet (or Mohammed) the Arab calendar had been of the early luni-solar type, i.e. with alternate months of 29 and 30 days, corrected from time to time by an intercalary month to keep the calendar in step with the seasons. The Koran suppresses this intercalary month 'for the number of months is twelve, as was ordained by Allah,' and shortly after the death of Mahomet the Moslem caliph Omar (caliph from 634 to 644), the conqueror of Egypt, Palestine, Syria and Persia, and the first 'Commander of the Faithful', instituted the new era based on the Koran. It dated from the first moon after the Prophet's flight from Mecca to Medina, which happened on July 16, in the year A.D. 622, a Friday, and Friday has since been the holy day of all holding the Mohammedan faith.

Because the calendar is strictly lunar, the Mohammedan year fails to keep step with the astronomical tropical year, and gains approximately one year in 33 on the Gregorian; thus, a person who would be described as 33 years of age by Moslem calculation would be about 32 under Gregorian rules.

For astronomical and chronological purposes the months are fixed by rule and not by observation. They have 30 and 29 days alternately, except the twelfth

117

month, which may have either 29 or 30 days. In a cycle of Mohammedan years, 19 are common years of 354 days, and eleven are leap years of 355 days. Thus 360 lunations are made equivalent to 10,631 days; as their real duration is 10,631·015 days, the error is extremely small.[1]

Observation, however, is still required for determining the start of the month for general and especially for religious purposes. A new month begins with the first sighting of the crescent of the new moon after sunset. No more interesting comment could be made on the impact of this fact on religious observance than the following from a recent biography of King Ibn Saud of Arabia[2] in which the author is dealing with the fast of Ramadan:

> There had been some discussion towards the end of the month as to the possibility of the new moon being seen after sunset on the 29th day; and after careful study of the *Nautical Almanac*, I had predicted that it would not be visible. Nevertheless the King sent two sharp-eyed Badawin to search the sky from the roof of the Ma'abida fort opposite the palace. They returned unsuccessful, but a flutter was created by two citizens of Mecca, who claimed to have seen the crescent, and were promptly sent by the King to give their evidence before the ecclesiastical court. Its verdict was negative; and, as no report of the sighting of the crescent had come in from any other quarter, it was decreed that there should be a thirtieth day of fasting.
>
> It should be mentioned that, since the establishment of the network of wireless stations referred to in a previous chapter, the range of possible sighting of the new moon has been greatly extended, with the result that such claims have become more frequent; the duty of determining their truth and reporting the result to headquarters by wireless being incumbent on

[1] Sir H. Spencer Jones, *The Calendar: Past, Present and Future* (1952).

[2] H. St. John Philby, *Arabian Jubilee* (Hale, 1952).

the local *Quadhis*, while the final decision rests with the King in consultation with the bishops of Mecca and Riyadh. It is a remarkable fact that the north-west corner of the country has almost always been the source of such reports of doubtful sightings: particularly the villages of 'Ula and Tabuk, whose experts have devized a method of their own for watching the motions of the crescent during the day. They put out a dish of water to catch the reflection of the sun and moon: and, if the latter is behind the former at noon, they follow both bodies till sunset, when they have a good chance of seeing the crescent if the sky is clear.

The months of the Mohammedan calendar, and the number of days (for chronological purposes) are:

1	Muharram	(30)	7	Rajab	(30)
2	Saphar	(29)	8	Shaaban	(29)
3	Rabia I	(30)	9	Ramadan	(30)
4	Rabia II	(29)	10	Shawwal	(29)
5	Jamada I	(30)	11	Dulkaada	(30)
6	Jamada II	(29)	12	Dulheggia	(29 or 30)

which make a total of 354 days (355 in leap year). The Mohammedan years are known as Hejira years and dates are prefixed with the letters A.H. (Anno Hejira). The leap year, of 355 days, is known as *kabishah*. The year A.H. 1372 began on September 21, 1952 by the Gregorian calendar. Whether a year is ordinary or *kabishah* can be worked out dividing its number by 30, and if the remainder is 2, 5, 7, 10, 13, 16, 18, 21, 24, 26, or 29, then it is a leap year, with 355 days. Because of the difference of eleven days between the Moslem and the Christian calendars, it is possible for the Hejira New Year—which is celebrated on Muharram 1—to arrive twice in a Gregorian year, as last happened in 1943, and occurs about every 32 years.

Looked at from a western point of view, the great disadvantage of the Mohammedan calendar is this retrogression through the seasons. A given date will, in the course of 32 of our years, or 33 Hejira years, fall in all the four seasons. For agricultural purposes therefore, the Moslem month and day differs with each consecutive year by eleven days, and sowing and reaping are never in the same place in the calendar twice.

However, Persia's story is not quite the same in this respect as that of other Moslem countries. After the conquest an important calendar reform was introduced. In the eleventh century, under the Sultan Malik Shah Jalal-al-Din, a great deal of interest was taken in astronomy, and around the Soldjuks of northern Persia were gathered a number of astronomers who had at their disposal a new observatory which had been founded by Malik Shah at al-Raiy or Nishapur.[1] Among them was the poet-astronomer Omar Khayyam.

The old pre-conquest Persian calendar had been, as Sarton puts it,[1] 'temporarily replaced' by the Moslem calendar. Malik Shah Jalal therefore called together a committee of astronomers, under the leadership of Omar Khayyam, to revise the old calendar. The result was the Jalili calendar, 'the best at that date recorded by mankind',[3] and described by Gibbon as 'a computation of time which surpasses the Julian and approaches the accuracy of the Gregorian style.[4]

This remarkable calendar began a new era, which was counted from 10th Ramadan 471 A.H., or 16th March A.D. 1079 but it was not destined to last long, and later the Mohammedan calendar was again introduced in the country. Unfortunately, its details are not known as well as one would like, for the book or monograph which Omar left on the subject has not survived, and there are

[1] *Encyclopedia of Islam*, Vol. I. Article on Astronomy.

[2] G. Sarton, *Introduction to the History of Science*, Vol. I. (Carnegie Institute of Washington, 1927.)

[3] Otto Rothfield, *Umar Khayyam and his Age* (Bombay 1922).

[4] Mirkhond, *History of the Assassins*, quoted in Golden Treasury edition of the *Rubaiyat*.

different versions of it. In his *Introduction to the History of Science*, Sarton remarks: 'There are many interpretations of Omar's reform and to each corresponds a certain degree of accuracy, but at any rate Omar's calendar was very accurate. The correct interpretation is probably one of the following, the second being the most probable. I quote for each the authority, the gist of the change, and then the resulting error:

> According to al-Shirazi (d. 1311), 17 intercalary days in 70 years; error, one day in about 1,550 years.
> According to Ulugh Beg (d. 1449), 15 intercalary days in 62 years; error, 1 day in about 3,770 years.
> 'Modern interpretation, 8 intercalary days in 32 years; error I day in about 5,000 years.

On the other hand, in his recent pamphlet on the history of the Calendar, the present Astronomer Royal assessed the proposal as having 'in effect, 31 leap years in a cycle of 128 years. The average length of the year is then 365·2421875 days, which is too short by 0·000012 days, or by about one second only'.

Although these details do not throw light on the internal division of the year in the Jalali calendar, they serve to show the high degree of Eastern scientific and astronomical knowledge of the period—which was about the time William the Conqueror invaded England. And they are all the more interesting because it is in Persia that a new calendar reform has been not only attempted, but instituted in this present century.

When Rizi Shah Pahlevi came to power in Persia in the early nineteen twenties he sought to introduce western ideas to a large extent, and one of these was an effort to adjust the 354-day Moslem calendar to the 365-day Gregorian. In his recent book *The Persian Language*[1] Professor Levy explains that in corresponding with

---

[1] R. Levy, *The Persian Language* (Hutchinson, 1951).

European or Europeanized fellow-countrymen, Persians are apt to date their letters according to the European calendar, using the French forms—janvier, fevrier, etc.—of the months. Normally, however, private letters are dated according to the Hijira era of the Mohammedan calendar. Shah Rizi sought to synthesize the two systems, while retaining well-established features of the traditional calendar of the country.

Abandoning the strictly lunar reckoning of alternative 29- and 30-day months, he brought into use a solar calendar still of twelve months but with their lengths re-adjusted to make a total of 365 days in the year, and with early Persian names which have never fallen entirely out of use. The first six months were to have 31 days each, the seventh to eleventh 30 days each, and the twelfth month 29 except in leap year when it has 30. The year begins conveniently at the vernal equinox. The new months are:

1.	Farvardin-mah	beginning	21st or 22nd March
2.	Ardibahisht-mah	,,	21st or 22nd April
3.	Khordad-Mah	,,	22nd or 23rd May
4.	Tir-mah	,,	22nd or 23rd June
5.	Mordan-mah	,,	23rd or 24th July
6.	Shartvar-mah	,,	23rd or 24th August
7.	Mehr-mah	,,	23rd or 24th September
8.	Aban-mah	,,	23rd or 24th October
9.	Azar-mah	,,	22nd or 23rd November
10.	Dai-mah	,,	22nd or 23rd December
11.	Bahman-mah	,,	21st or 22nd January
12.	Esfand-mah		
	(Esfandarmoz)	,,	20th or 21st February

'The new era', says Professor Levy, 'was entitled the *Sale Hejra Shamsi* and the new date was arrived at by taking the Christian year and subtracting from it the number 622 (year of the Hijrah) for dates between January 1 and March 20 or 21, and 621 if it lies between

21 (22) of March and 31 December. Thus *Now Ruz*
of the year 1302 (Hijrah year) corresponded with 22
March 1923; 25 Bahman 1323 corresponded with 14
February 1945; *Now Ruz* 1925 corresponded with 21
March 1946; 12 Farvardin 1325 with 1 April 1946'.

Now Ruz is the Persian New Year, the celebrations of
which last for thirteen days.

Admirable as this reform would appear to be in its
approach to the problem of harmonizing the two most
widely used calendars in the world—at least a step
forward towards a world calendar—it seems not to have
had any appeal to other Mohammedan countries, and it
is doubtful if it is used outside the boundaries of Iran.
It is used on official documents in that country and
newspapers originating there employ it, some bearing
the Mohammedan, the 'reformed' and the European
dates, but in private correspondence between Persians
and the inhabitants of other Moslem countries, it is
pretty certain that the Mohammedan (lunar) dating
would be used.

CHAPTER V

The Vexed Question of Easter

B Y 1 9 3 1 T H E League of Nations had still not made up its corporate or even its committee mind. But it had put in more than eight years of study and it had got together a lot of appropriate information. It issued another Report. This was officially a 'Preparatory Document', prepared for the Fourth General Conference on Communications and Transit, and it analysed neatly the position at the time of the various national committees that had gone into the matter. In fact, it lined up the countries for and against reform, which was very useful; and it did something else, equally important: it began to indicate a sharp separation in practice of two phases of the subject which previously had been considered as part of the same thing, but now were turning out to be two different things—the question of calendar reform, and the question of a fixed Easter.

The passing in the meantime of the Easter Act 1928 in Britain had much to do with creating this separation, and if, so far, it has proved completely useless in achieving the purpose for which it was passed, the Act has at least shown that the fixed Easter question need not affect the calendar reform problem as a whole. To that extent it has done some good. It cannot be too strongly emphasized that calendar revision can be brought about completely outside the Easter question. The two things are, as the League was now finding out, two things.

From the beginning, the League had this Easter problem closely in mind; had regarded it, in fact, as an integral part of the matter they were to investigate, and on which they were to make recommendations. This was natural enough; the Chambers of Commerce and other bodies passing the resolutions which had much to do with the taking up of the calendar reform question by the League had almost invariably stressed this side of the problem. In some instances it had been their whole case.

In the preamble to their Report of 1926, the League Committee had put the case of the disadvantages of the non-fixity of Easter very well:

The date of Easter varies at present between March 22nd and April 25th, *i.e.*, over a period of thirty-five days, and involves a corresponding displacement of the movable festivals. Numerous disadvantages result, both from a civil and a religious point of view. In the civil sphere, school, university and judicial work, and commercial interests, including these relating to transport, are particularly affected. The beginning of the scholastic year and some of its holidays are fixed, whereas others are movable. The same disadvantages apply to judicial or administrative holidays.

Many commercial transactions and the transport services connected with them are severely prejudiced by the changing date of Easter: in particular, business dealing with textiles, articles of fashion and the hotel-keeping industry, since Easter marks the beginning of the spring fashions and is an important date from the tourist point of view.

If Easter is early, the weather of the Northern Hemisphere being unfavourable in the temperate zones at this time of the year, travelling and changes in dress are postponed. If, on the other hand, Easter is late, there is more tourist business, but the textile trade in spring wear is severely injured, because summer articles are purchased at once. In a general way the organization of traffic and transport is disturbed by the changing date of Easter.

From the religious point of view, there are disadvantages due to the fact that the number of Sundays in the year being practically fixed, the services of the Roman Catholic liturgy which cannot take place before Easter when this festival is early have to be postponed until after Whitsuntide.'

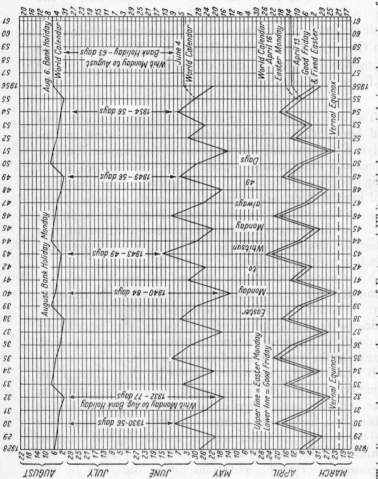

This diagram shows how the dates of Easter and Whitsuntide have varied since the passing of the inoperative Easter Act 1928, and the wide variation in the intervals between Whit Monday and August Bank Holiday. Under the World Calendar, and with a Fixed Easter (as provided for in the Act) these wildly oscillating lines would straighten out and the intervals between holidays become perfectly regular. The change could suitably be made in 1956 when January 1 falls on Sunday, and the old and new calendars would coincide. A similar opportunity will not occur

The Committee then adds that it 'found itself obliged to separate the question of the fixing of Easter from that of the general reform of the calendar'. In spite of this, no study of the calendar can avoid taking some account of this vexed Easter question.

As long ago as 1884, Armelin had suggested April 7 as a fixed date for Easter in his prize-winning calendar. In 1896 the Director of the Berlin Observatory, who was also president of the International Committee on Weights and Measures, had addressed a circular to scientific, religious and political bodies on the desirability of stabilizing Easter, and the matter had in general been associated with calendar reform. One of the League's early actions when it undertook the calendar investigation had been to send out to its member governments and to important bodies a questionnaire to open the subject, and one of the questions asked had inevitably concerned itself with this business of Easter. The question was, in effect: 'Are you in favour of a fixed date for Easter?'

The recorded replies are voluminous: it is beyond the scope of this work to attempt to recapitulate or even to summarize them, but it can be definitely stated that secular opinion was overwhelmingly in favour of Easter being fixed, or at any rate stabilized.[1] Almost unanimously, however, governments, authorities, and often, where any comment was made, even in commercial circles, it was conceded that it was basically a religious question, and that the decision must be dependent on agreement of the churches.

[1] Naturally, if the question of Easter is separated from that of the general reform of the calendar or, to be more accurate, that of establishing a perpetual calendar, the term 'fixing' in the strict sense of the word could not be applied to the reform scheme; the expression 'stabilization' is the only correct term, because, if the calendar is not perpetual and if, as is almost universally considered, Easter must fall on a Sunday, its date will unavoidably oscillate within a seven-day period—*League's 1931 Report.*

The strength of the demand for the stabilization of Easter is unmistakable, the consensus of approval in principle overwhelming. Yet it does not take place, and this in spite of the fact that there is practically no formal opposition from the churches, either.

It is an extraordinary situation, nowhere stranger than in Britain. Here an Act was passed in 1928 which was designed to carry out this obvious and much-needed reform, subject to the proviso that 'regard shall be had to any opinion officially expressed by any Church or other Christian body'. But no action has been taken. It is doubtful if history has on record any other case of an Act of Parliament, passed and accepted by the country, and yet never put into operation directly or indirectly.

The Act is very short. It reads as follows:

1. Easter-day shall, in the calendar year next but one after the commencement of this Act and in all subsequent years, be the first Sunday after the second Saturday in April, and section three of the Calendar (New Style) Act, 1750, the new calendar, tables and rules annexed to that Act, and section two of the Calendar Act, 1751, are hereby amended and shall be read and construed accordingly, and, in particular, the Calendar (New Style) Act, 1750, shall, as respects such calendar years as aforesaid, have effect as if in the 'Rules to know when the Moveable Feasts and Holy Days begin' contained in that Act, for the words 'is always the first Sunday after the full moon which happens upon or next after the twenty-first day of March, and if the full moon happens upon a Sunday, Easter Day is the Sunday after,' there shall be substituted the words 'is always the first Sunday after the second Saturday in April.'

2. (1) This Act may be cited as the Easter Act, 1928.

(2) This Act shall commence and come into operation on such date as shall be fixed by Order of His Majesty in Council, provided that, before any such Order in Council is made, a draft thereof shall be laid before both Houses of Parliament, and the Order shall not be made unless both Houses by resolution approve the draft either without modification or with

modifications to which both Houses agree, but upon such approval being given the order may be made in the form in which it has been so approved; Provided further that, *before making such draft order, regard shall be had to any opinion officially expressed by any Church or other Christian body.*

There was a third clause setting out the various parts of the Commonwealth to which the Act might be extended, by further orders-in-council. That was all. It was quite clear. Easter in Britain had been stabilized, and under the Act would in future be celebrated between the 8th and the 15th of April, aside from any question of a general revision of the calendar. But before the required Order could be made to put the improvement into operation 'regard' had to be taken of the opinion of the churches.

Of course there had already been such 'regard'. It is inconceivable that such an Act could have got to the Statute Book without it. The following statement[1] sets out the attitude of the Church of England:

The question of a fixed date for Easter in the Kalendar of the Book of Common Prayer was considered in 1924 by the Convocation of York, which appointed a Joint Committee (which seems never to have reported). It was considered on April 28th, 1925, by the Convocation of Canterbury when both Houses agreed

1. That there is no dogmatic reason why the Church should oppose a fixed date for Easter, but the Church of England could not consent to the proposed change unless it was accepted by the other Christian Communions.

2. That if a fixed Easter were adopted, April should be assigned for the Festival, which should fall on a Sunday, approximately midway between the present limits of variation.

[1] Church Information Board, in a letter to the author, January 22 1952.

3. That it is important to take into account the whole sequence of the Church's year in considering any proposals for fixing Easter, and particularly for any general reconstruction of the Kalendar.

After the passing of the Act, the Church varied its opinion as to the most suitable dates for celebration, and the same authority states:

On 14th February, 1929, both Houses of Canterbury agreed:

> In the event of general ecclesiastical concurrence with the object of the Easter Act, 1928, this House is of opinion that the first Sunday in April should be adopted as Easter Day.

YORK

The same resolution was adopted by the Upper House of York and communicated to the Lower House.

In the League's 1931 Report the position of the other Christian churches was summarized. The Orthodox Church would be prepared to pronounce in favour, *subject to a common agreement between the churches*: eighty-two Protestant Churches in twenty countries were *either in favour or had declared themselves ready to adopt* a fixed Easter: The Holy See had stated that 'any changes which might be made as regards the fixing of Easter, *though they would meet with no difficulties from the point of view of dogma*, would nevertheless involve the abandonment of deeply-rooted traditions' . . . 'but agreed that if it were demonstrated that the fixing of Easter *would be universally beneficial* it was ready to submit the question to an Oecumenical Council'.

There the matter remained, and still remains.

Although the net result of the 30-years campaign had been, by 1931, completely to separate the Easter question from that of calendar reform in general and to place this abortive Act on the Statute Book, it is interesting to

glance quickly at two attempts which have been made in
recent years to obtain some action. Lord Merthyr introduced a Motion in the House of Lords on February 15
1951, 'that this House, taking into consideration the fact
that an Act to regulate the date of Easter Day has been
on the statute book since 1928, but has since that date
been inoperative in consequence of subsection two of
section two of the Act, is of opinion that the Act should
now be brought into force by the repeal of the aforesaid
sub-section'.[1] There was a long debate in which the
Archbishop of Canterbury re-stated the Anglican case,
and the Earl of Iddesleigh put forward the Roman
Catholic attitude. One statement made by Lord Iddesleigh revealed the unlikelihood of agreement in the fore-
seeable future. Quoting the Vatican's message to the
effect that 'if it were shown that the general good
demands some change . . . the Holy See would not be
willing to examine the question without the preliminary
opinion of a General (Oecumencal) Council', he went on:

> That, my Lords, was the message sent to the League of
> Nations in 1924. In 1928 a somewhat similar statement was
> issued. In that second statement, however, the words: 'the
> forthcoming General Council' were used. I should explain to
> your Lordships that at the end of the 1920's, and the beginning
> of the 1930's, it appears to have been in the mind of Pope
> Pius XI that the time was opportune for the convocation of
> another General Council, the last having been held in 1870.
> But the course of temporal history in the 1930's rendered that
> hope nugatory; and there seems no hope today whatever of
> any General Council being summoned.

Lord Merthyr withdrew his motion, which also had
been nugatory, and the next that was heard of the subject
in Parliamentary circles was a motion by Sir Richard
Acland a few weeks later, in the House of Commons.

[1] *House of Lords Official Report* (Hansard) February 15 1951.

Sir Richard, learning from the discouragement of the Peers, tackled the problem another way. Whereas Lord Merthyr had sought to *repeal* the suspending clause in the Act, Acland moved to bring in a Bill to *amend* it. He proposed the alteration of the clause in such a way that the Act would become operative in the following year, so that in due course it would apply to the Easter of 1954 (under Clause 1 no Easter is affected 'until the next calendar year but one after it comes into operation'). Sir Richard explained how his amendment would work:[1]

> No religious denomination would be in any way coerced. But the onus of taking positive action of some kind would be shifted. Today the onus of taking positive action rests upon those who would like to see Easter and Whitsun more narrowly confined. . . . Were my Bill to become law, the position would be that the religious denominations would have a period of one and three-quarter years during which, if they were so minded, they could put forward their objections towards this proposal.

The debate that followed was not a long one—it lasted less than half an hour—nor were any sound objections raised. The House divided, and Sir Richard's motion was carried by 279 votes to 105, which would appear to have been an extremely encouraging result, but the Bill was dropped and nothing further done.

There the matter rests.

[1] Hansard, March 19 1952.

CHAPTER VI

The Solstitial Start

ON WHAT DATE should time begin?

It would seem a little late to ask the question now, but it has been asked often enough before, and who is to say whether there has ever been a satisfactory answer? The Old Testament gives a specific date for Creation as a beginning of Jewish history. The Romans began their counting from the assumed date of the foundation of Rome, though the very word 'date' implies that something must have gone before. Greek time-reckoning made use of the Olympic Games. The Mohammedan Calendar counts from the Prophet's flight to Medina. Innumerable eras for innumerable calendars have started either at some arbitrarily selected moment, or to mark an event, or to register a dynasty, or the accession of a monarch or dictator. In France, Time got a new start with the Revolution.

That new beginning in France had one attribute that starts of other eras have lacked. It is true that its inception was for the purpose of enclosing an historical event, but in carrying out this purpose, those who devised it sensibly made it dependent on astronomical facts as well as revolutionary exuberance. Perhaps the only 'era'— short-lived as it was—which has done so, except the Moslem, which began at the moment of visibility of a new moon. In the French case, it may have been a fortunate coincidence that an outstanding event in the revolution—the Proclamation of the Republic—coincided with the autumn equinox, but it was scientific knowledge which decided the actual moment of the start of the new annual reckoning at that point in time.

Strictly, that is astronomically, speaking, there are only four points at which time reckoning by solar years should properly begin—the two solstices and the two equinoxes—the moments when the sun is in its most northerly and southerly positions, and the two occasions in the year when day and night are equal. Of these the solstices are preferable, for they mark each an exact instant. They occur on or about June 22, when the sun is at its farthest northern point, and December 22 when it is farthest south. (One has to say 'on or about' because the Gregorian calendar is not perfect, and over a long period is shifting the date, slowly moving these dates away from the solstices).

Since astrology gave place to astronomy these facts have always been present in the minds of calendar-makers, but politics, religion and history have usually had far more to do with the matter. However, it was very much present in the deliberations of the League of Nations calendar committee, on which the science of astronomy was well represented. When the committee set out to get the nations' views on calendar reform it made this one of the questions, and in the first circular to member countries it enclosed the minutes of a meeting of the International Astronomical Union of which the following is an extract:

> *The Moment at which the Year should begin.* The Chairman (M. Bigourdan) explained that the present beginning of the year, which occurred about ten days after the winter solstice, was arbitrarily chosen, and that by putting January 1st at the date which at present was December 22nd, it would be possible to make the quarters and the astronomical seasons correspond more exactly, which would be an advantage at any rate so far as statistics were concerned. The chairman went on to say that Julius Cæsar would have put his January 1st at the winter

solstice had he not been afraid that this might jeopardize the adoption of his reform.

M. Deslandres was of opinion that January 1st should be put back to December 22nd. Father Rodes, MM. Delaporte, Miller, Armand Baar, and de la Baume-Pluvinel supported this proposal. M. Nijland and Father Stein, on the other hand, thought January 1st should not be interefered with. The secretary read a passage from the memorandum sent in by M. Eginitis, of Athens, in which he said that 'it was not practical to change the date of the beginning of the year'.

Abbé Chauve-Bertrand said that when the Gregorian reform was introduced, papal commissioners had proposed the suppression not only of ten days but of thirteen, with a view to fixing Christmas on the exact day of the winter solstice. He added that in that case Christmas and not January 1st was in question, but as the latter festival was also regarded as the religious New Year, this was a further argument in favour of beginning the year at the winter solstice.

The proposal to begin the year on December 22nd was put to the vote and carried by a majority.

The astronomical point of view was therefore not in doubt, but one imagines that the question must have caused considerable scratching of heads in the sixty-odd government offices in which it was asked. This looked like calendar reform with a vengeance. It was all very well for the astronomers to want a new start for a new year, but what would be the practical results? What about the old year, which would finish on December 21, losing ten days? It would be 1582, or 1752, or some other Gregorian date over again. And what advantage would be gained, beyond pleasing the astronomers?

In due course the answers began to come in:

From Albania: It would not appear to be practical to set back the commencement of the year to a date nine days before the present January 1st. Although this change might be of some use to Catholics, it would, on the contrary, cause much embarrassment to the Orthodox Church.

From Finland: There are not sufficient reasons for putting January 1st at the date which is at present December 22nd, because in any case the quarters do not agree with the astronomic seasons and still less with the vegetal seasons.

From Germany: Neither the representatives of science nor of commercial life consider that in Germany there is any practical need to carry back the beginning of the year to the day corresponding to December 22nd. The German Government recommends that this change should not be made.

From Greece: To place the beginning of the year on the day now occupied by December 22nd is a modification which, without serving any practical purpose, would have the result of making New Year's Day precede the Christmas Festival, which is inadmissible from the ecclesiastical point of view.

From Italy: (Director of the Royal Observatory, Rome): I regret that I am unable to agree with the Geneva Committee, which desires to place the first day of the year at the winter solstice.

From the Netherlands: There are serious objections to the proposal that the beginning of the year should be set back from January 1st to the winter solstice. It is to be feared that a jump of ten days would cause a very undesirable break in the continuity of all statistics. . . .

And so on through the international alphabet. Not a favourable word until we reach South Africa, which supported the view of the Astronomical Union. Most of the countries ignored or slid over the question, and one or two left the decision on this, like other points, to the Churches, but hardly was there a friendly word for this purely scientific reform. Even the Italian astronomer, whose report had been forwarded by his Government, had not agreed with his fellow astronomers.

It was not surprising that the preparatory report for the 4th Conference in 1931 contained the words

'Eliminating, as was done by the Special Committee, any scheme which changes the beginning of the year. . . .'— and forgot it.

But the last had not been heard of the astronomical inexactitude of the present calendar. At the same conference and arising out of the same item there was put forward a case for the revision of the leap year rule.

Now in the United States there had been created a National Committee on Calendar Simplification, which had undoubtedly gone very seriously and deeply into all the aspects of the calendar problem as applied to modern conditions and affairs. Moreover it had treated the matter with the full weight of modern scientific knowledge. Not content with a temporary adjustment, it had looked forward to the future—even the far future. It dealt with the calendar as, in the definition of its Vice-Chairman, Dr Charles F. Marvin, Chief of the United States Weather Bureau, 'a device of civilization which should register the passage of time for a great many centuries in close accord with solar and astronomical conditions.'

It was a contribution to the League Committee by Dr. Marvin (and published by the League as a Supplement)[1] which directed official attention to the imperfection of the Gregorian leap year rule for keeping the years in correct step with the cycle of the seasons for all time, or at least for a very long time. It showed, incidentally, that no simple leap-year rule would do that, in any case, for *the length of the year is changing*. Not much, but changing just the same.

'Two important questions require consideration', stated this contribution, which was in the form of a Discussion by Dr. Marvin, 'but they are quite distinct and may be acted upon separately or together. They are of a purely technical nature. First it will be shown . . . that the Gregorian leap year rule furnishes almost perfect

[1] League of Nations Publications VIII Transit, 1931, VIII. 12/I Supplement.

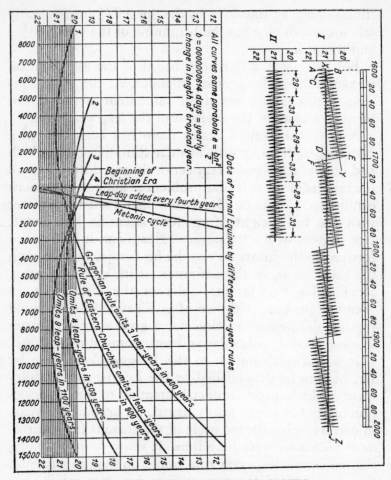

HOW THE VERNAL EQUINOX MOVES

The diagram indicates the fundamental difficulty of maintaining the calendar
without adjustment over a long period. Because of the slight change in the
length of the day, over the next 15,000 years the Gregorian leap-year system
(dropping 3 leap-year days every 400 years) will bring the Vernal Equinox back
to March 11, but under the system adopted by the Eastern Orthodox Church
(dropping 7 leap-year days in 900 years) it will have moved only to March 15
The other two curves are theoretical only, the best being one which omits 9
leap-year days in 1,100 years. The right-hand part of the dagram illustrates (I)
the effect on the Equinox of the dropping of the centennial leap-year days in
the Gregorian calendar over a period of 400 years; and (II) an ideal (theoretical)
method of keeping the calendar in step (and the Vernal Equinox always at
March 21) by having 15 leap-days in 62 years—a system, however, which would
require a complicated table to keep track of which were ordinary years and
which leap years.

reckoning for all past time from 9000 B.C. to the present, but that the rule is beginning to fail—it is outliving its usefulness; and, second, the nominal date of the vernal equinox is now March 21st, intended to be the same as at the time of the Council of Nicæa, A.D. 325. However, its actual average date is more nearly March 20th. Shall this date be changed, and, if so, what shall the date be?'

It gives a brief history of the Julian calendar and then the Discussion points out that 'counting from the beginning of the Christian era, the dislocation of the equinox amounted to over 12 days in Gregory's time, only a part of which was adjusted by dropping 10 days when the Gregorian reform went into effect in October of 1582.

'While far superior to the Julian rule, especially for calendar reckoning over past centuries, Gregory's rule also intercalates too many leap days, especially in the future, and the date of the equinox is gradually falling earlier.'

It then commented that the Greek Church, which did not abandon the Julian calendar until 1923, had improved on the calculations of the sixteenth century. 'A notable feature of this reform is that it includes a new leap-year rule which is a bit more accurate for future reckoning than the Gregorian one'. So that it seems the best calendar extant is that of the Orthodox Church. (But it does nothing about the arrangement of the months within the year).

The diagram on page 138 which is reproduced from the League of Nations publication[1] shows how the vernal equinox (and with it of course the autumn equinox and the two solstices) is still gradually moving through the dates of March, at different rates according to the different leap year systems. Under the Gregorian calendar, the

[1] From the Discussion by Dr. Charles L. Marvin in the Supplementary Report of the Committee on Calendar Simplification of the United States submitted to the League of Nations. (1931. VIII. 12/1 Supplement.

difference is one day in about 3,000 years, but by the year A.D. 15,000 the calendar would, if not adjusted in the meantime, bring the vernal equinox back to March 11, which would set up again precisely the condition that prevailed in 1582, when ten days had to be dropped to restore it to the Nicean date of March 21. The error is effective very much more slowly than was the case with the Julian calendar, but it is there just the same.

Whereas the Gregorian rule omits three leap years in every 400 years (only the centennial years divisible by 400 are not leap years); the Eastern Orthodox rule omits seven in 900 years, which is the improvement Dr. Marvin referred to, and this produces a slower error. By the year A.D. 15,000, under that rule the equinox will be happening on March 15, having gained only six days. The other curves in the diagram show the operation of other suggestions which are theoretical only. One of these involves the combination of the Omar Khayyam rule (of eight leap years in every 33) with a series of seven leap years in 29 alternately. Its disadvantage is that instead of simplifying the calendar it would complicate it by requiring a table to keep the leap years in their right order.

From a layman's point of view perhaps all this does not matter. It would seem that the calendar can be corrected from time to time by the dropping of an appropriate leap year day, and since the rules are so well known, adequate arrangements to avoid disturbance can be made well in advance. But it is interesting, and it serves to illustrate the impossibility of devising the absolutely perfect, simple calendar over long periods as well as short. And for the benefit of the layman, it should perhaps be pointed out that the variation of the length of the year is not such as is likely to cause any perturbation. It is due, Dr. Marvin points out, to the combined attractions of other planets which cause 'small secular variations in the motions of the earth as a result of which the eccentricity of its orbit, its inclination to the plane of the ecliptic, and the precession of its nodal points undergo periodic secular changes'. Two eminent French astronomers, Le Verrier and Gailbt, and an American astronomer, Simon Newcomb, have computed the rate of change in the length of the tropical year, and arrived at a figure of approximately (minus) 0·00000006 of a day. This is a very small fraction of a second, but considered over thousands of years, it is enough to cause the variations shown in the curves of the diagram.

CHAPTER VII

Enter the World Calendar

IN THE EARLY 'thirties the prestige and importance
of the League of Nations was still high, and it was still
tremendously active in good work. In spite of this, its
investigation of the calendar problem had not got anywhere at the turn of the decade—or at least not very far.
The committee on calendar reform had certainly inter-
viewed a good many people and had acquired an immense amount of data, but no definite decisions had been
reached; no formal recommendations to the nations had
been made.

However, the report to which we have referred
appeared in 1931. It was in the form of a 'Report of the
Preparatory Committee' for presentation to the Fourth
General Conference on Communications and Transit of
the League, and was the report which, as has been indicated, firmly separated the Easter question from the
general calendar situation. It went further in that it
narrowed down 'Schemes of Reform' to two headings,
which it described as

(a) Equalization of the Quarters without establishing a
Perpetual Calendar; and

(b) Perpetual Calendar involving 364 days bearing Week-
day Names, plus one Supplementary Day (Two in Leap
Years) not bearing the name of a Weekday.

This (b) heading then got another sub-division, for it is
reported that the Committees (there had been two by this
time—a Special Committee and a National Committee)

142

'in considering calendar proposals involving the introduction of a 'supplementary' day or days, devoted their consideration exclusively to the two following plans of reform:

(1) Thirteen months of 28 days; and

(2) Twelve months each containing 30 or 31 days'.

Thus had the several hundred schemes (more had now been received than the original 185 of the 1927 report) that had come up for consideration boiled down to three practical propositions. Also the question of altering the start of the year to one of the 'natural' dates —the equinoxes or the solstices—had been completely dropped. So to this extent it may perhaps be said that some progress had been made; the practical had been sorted out from the impractical. And what was equally interesting was the fact that the twelve-month perpetual plan now was put forward equally prominently with the thirteen-month proposal which had then been vigorously advocated for more than twenty years, and almost without a rival, by Mr. Moses Cotsworth and his strongly supported International Fixed Calendar League.

The reason for this was mainly the incursion into the field of a new authority, with a new, clear-cut proposal. That proposal was the World Calendar, and the authority the World Calendar Association which had been founded by Elisabeth Achelis in New York to promulgate a plan which should embody the best features of the various twelve-month, equal-quarter schemes which had been put forward to date. Miss Achelis had herself appeared before the League Committee and stated her case for her calendar. This World Calendar has since 1931 made practically all the running in the campaign for reform. But before dealing with it in detail it is worth while to examine the three propositions to which the report directed the attention of the then forthcoming Conference.

Taking first its heading (a), it deals with *Equalization of the Quarters without establishing a Perpetual Calendar.* Here the suggestion is the approximate equalization of the quarters, which in its simplest way could be done by taking certain days off the long months and putting them on the short ones, as for example in the Alexander Philip proposal (although this is not mentioned by name specifically) of taking a day from August and placing it at the end of February. Such reforms, says the report, 'involve only the difficulties inherent in any reform of whatever nature'.

Against them, 'the only question which they raise and which, indeed, has been raised, is whether their advantages would justify a change'.

So much for (a); now we come to (b), the *Perpetual Calendar with Supplementary day or days*, and its sub-division into two opposing principles—Thirteen months, or Twelve. Here the report goes into much greater detail, and sets out the *pros* and *cons* of both suggestions, obviously with the intention of being perfectly fair to both. It is only just that we should do the same.

The reason, the report begins by explaining, why the calendar is not perpetual is that a year consists of 52 weeks plus one day (or two days in leap year). This difficulty would be remedied by reducing ordinary years to 364 days and adding a 'supplementary' week in certain years. But such a calendar—proposed by certain representatives of religious authorities opposed to a break in the continuity of the week—would . . . be inferior to the present calendar, *and cannot be considered at all.*[1] Any scheme of reform instituting a perpetual calendar without changing the length of the Gregorian year thus necessarily means that one day in the year (or two in leap year) must be regarded as supplementary. . . .

Having eliminated, therefore, 'any scheme which changes the beginning of the year or divides the year into months of considerably different length', the report goes on to consider (1) and (2) of (b), setting out the advantages and disadvantages claimed by the opposing sides:

[1] My italics.

(1) *Thirteen months of twenty-eight days.*

| *Advantages* | *Disadvantages* |

Advantages

1. Each month has the same number of days; each month has the same number of days of the same name; each month has, with the exception of civil and religious holidays, the same number of working days.

2. Each month has the same number of whole weeks and no month contains fractions of a week at the beginning or the end. Each quarter has thirteen weeks.

3. Discrepancies between the days of the week and the dates in successive months and years are avoided. It is easier to fix permanent dates for public meetings, law court sessions, educational courses, etc.

4. The periods for which monthly salaries are calculated correspond with the periods of expenditure. Family and business budgets are simplified.

5. The months are all comparable with the exception of holidays, and, since they contain an equal number of days and no fractions of weeks, require no adjustment. Wage payments for parts of weeks (in the case of monthly salaries) are avoided. Office work is considerably lessened and economy can be made when preparing book-keeping or statistical reports, in private or public business and certain scientific occupations, and in reckoning servants' wages.

Disadvantages

1. The number thirteen is not divisible by 2, 3, 4 or 6.

2. The quarters and half-years (at present comprising three months and six months respectively) would not contain a whole number of months.

3. There would be thirteen monthly business balancings and thirteen monthly payments instead of twelve, involving to a certain extent increased work in connection with book-keeping and payments.

4. During the period of transition, this plan would mean a greater number of adjustments in comparing statistics and dates than would be necessary under the twelve-month system.

(2) *Twelve months each containing thirty or thirty-one days.*

Advantages	*Disadvantages*
1. The half-years and quarters are equal and have a whole number of months and weeks—*i.e.*, thirteen weeks in the quarter.	1. The months are not of the same length and are not directly comparable. Moreover, they differ as to the number and economic value of individual week-days—*e.g.*, one may have five Saturdays and another five Sundays.
2. Quarters and half-years, with the exception of civil and religious holidays, can be statistically compared without adjustments for varying lengths.	2. It would seem less essential to equalize the half-years and quarters than the months, since accountings for these periods are less frequent and less important than monthly accountings.
3. This system would involve little disturbance in established traditions and would involve less difficulty in the period of transition.	3. The months do not contain a complete number of weeks, payments for fractions of a week at the end of a month where payments are made monthly.
	4. The dates do not fall on the same day of the week in each month.

There is the whole case of the Battle of the Months—the twelve-month calendar *v.* the thirteen-month. At this time it seemed to be the only question really in dispute, for it is implicit throughout the whole report that the two League committees who had considered the matter found reform desirable. And disregarding the Easter controversy (by this time separated out of the general case) it had become remarkably clear, crystal clear, that revolutionary changes—decimal calendars, supplementary *weeks*, philosophical nomenclatures, five-day or six-day weeks, solstitial starts of the years, or anything else that interfered drastically with the historical sequence of time—were 'out'. The implication was that though obviously neither the twelve-month nor the thirteen-month proposals was a perfect answer—each had its disadvantages as well as its advantages—at least they were *practical*, whereas the other schemes were either impractical, or, where they could be put into practice, offered such slight improvements over the existing calendar that they would not be worth even the minor disruption they might be expected to cause.

It is an interesting sidelight at this point too, that these official bodies—the League committees—had ceased now to refer to the 'blank' days that had been a feature of earlier reports. They had become 'supplementary' days, and 'extra-calendrical' days. While the Jewish or other religious opponents of either scheme, or any perpetual scheme involving a re-adjustment of the 365th (and 366th) days of the years, continued to speak (and still continue to speak) of 'blank' days as though there was something derogatory, or perhaps even a little indecent, about them, since they fell necessarily outside of an ordinary week, the official view seemed to have accepted their necessity as a scientific and perfectly respectable requirement.

So the problem was presented, fair and square, for further consideration, and the next few years were to be devoted to its argument. At this time, so far as public opinion could be ascertained, the majority view was rather in favour of the thirteen-month idea, which was not surprising considering the long campaign which had been so enthusiastically carried on by Mr. Cotsworth. However, the twelve-month proposal, in one or other of its forms (31, 30, 30 or 30, 30, 31) had its proponents too, and the World Calendar Association was also now devoting itself, with unquenchable vigour and reasoned argument, to advocating the nearest-to-perfect twelve-month, equal-quarters (31, 30, 30) plan and setting out to combat the conspicuous public apathy on the whole question.

This apathy on the part of people, even those people who would undoubtedly benefit from reform, is the major obstacle which was then (and still is) holding back the whole matter of calendar reform. In no case has this been more so than in Britain, as we shall see, and at this time it loomed large in official considerations. In view of later developments and to show how wide had been the inquiry, it is worth quoting a part of this 1931 League Report on the situation as it seemed then to be:

The disadvantages of the existing calendar are not disputed in any report (from the various countries), but, as regards public opinion in their respective countries, it would appear from the reports submitted by the French, British and Italian committees, as well as from oral information given by the representative of the Argentine national committee, that public opinion as a whole does not seem keenly interested in calendar reform.

The British committee finds that public opinion, whether general or particular, is little interested in plans for calendar reform, apart from the stabilization of Easter.

All the members of the Italian committee, while considering that Italy cannot remain outside a movement for the simplification of the calendar . . . think that the time is not yet favourable for carrying out this reform and that its advantages still appear problematical and its disadvantages serious. On the other hand, according to the German committee's report, the necessity for a reform of the existing calendar is generally recognized in Germany.

The work of the United States committee gives a similar impression as regards the question of calendar reform by the American public. Of the 1,433 replies received to the questionnaire,[1] 80·5 per cent are in favour of the calendar simplification and 82 per cent declared themselves in favour of the participation of the United States in an international conference on calendar reform.

[1] The U.S. and other national committees had sent out questionnaires on the subject to public bodies and periodicals in their own countries.

The Swedish committee considers that it is essential to proceed cautiously in the matter. The Swiss national committee is of opinion that the simplification of the Gregorian calendar is both desirable and expedient so long as no more changes are made in the habits and customs of the people than are really necessary. Of the replies received, 93 per cent are in favour of a simplified calendar.

The Portuguese committee states that, although the public is somewhat apathetic with regard to the question, the replies received to the questionnaire which it sent out show, in its opinion, that the Portuguese public as a whole is favourable to reform.

Lastly, the Brazilian committee's report seems to show that public opinion in Brazil is favourable to reform.

Much more detail about questionnaires sent out and national scientific, industrial, religious, educational and cultural organizations consulted was given, but this quick sample gives a reasonable assessment of the public attitude throughout the important countries, and that had been roughly the situation when that ardent reformer Elisabeth Achelis, and her new-founded Association came on the scene, a year or so earlier. How that happened, Miss Achelis has told in her own book.[1]

She relates how during a vacation she attended as a matter of passing interest a lecture by Dr. Melvil Dewey, on 'How to Simplify Life', and how one of the simplifications propounded by the famous inventor of the universal library catalogue was that of the Gregorian calendar. But Dr. Dewey was a proponent of the thirteen-month calendar, and the disadvantages of this struck her much more forcibly than the advantages. She was persuaded of the need for reform, but, she writes, 'as he elaborated I became increasingly indignant. How could the prime number thirteen ever simplify? How could such an arbitrary and indivisible number ever

[1] Elisabeth Achelis, *The Calendar for Everybody* (Putnam, New York, 1943).

replace the convenient 12? I left the lecture feeling decidedly uneasy. . . .'

However, she would probably have forgotten it, except for seeing a little later a letter in the *New York Times* on the subject. It came from a Mr. Lewis E. Ashburgh, of Denver, who wrote, *inter alia*: 'While we are planning an improved calendar, let us also insist on the very best, with all conditions considered, and let us adopt the revised twelve-month year of equal quarters and equal working-day months, easily adapted *from the calendar we now use.*'

The result was the discovery of a useful field of work and a decision to devote herself exclusively to it. She concentrated on a study of the subject reading all the available material at her disposal in the libraries and fascinated, no doubt (as are all who delve deep enough), by the intensely interesting lore of the calendar. She made herself acquainted with the scientific aspect and the trend of modern thought and research on the matter. She became a specialist and an expert. After some months of this serious consideration of the subject it was not unnatural that she should come to a firm decision as to (*a*) the urgent need for calendar reform (though that presumably she had never doubted from the beginning), and (*b*) the direction such reform should take. She rejected the thirteen-month calendar as too disturbing of established practice, and sought a more practical plan which by avoiding any major disruption of conventional usage would have a reasonable prospect of acceptance and yet fulfil the essential requirements of desirable reform.

She evolved the World Calendar, a twelve-months, equal-quarter calendar which possessed the highly important quality of being capable of exact repetition year after year and, for practical purposes, quarter after quarter, with a minimum of disadvantages and disturbance. She does not, of course, claim to have invented it;

rather it is a synthesis of the best features of all the twelve-month calendars that had been proposed since Armelin.

However, many people might have devoted as much thought and interest to the subject, and have got as far as this satisfying conclusion—indeed, they have—and then have been unable to do more than bring it to the world's notice through, perhaps, letters to the Press or such usual channels of dissemination of knowledge and opinion. Miss Achelis happened to be more fortunately placed and was happily in a position to give the proposal adequate financial support also. She reports that 'in the autumn (of 1930) with the aid of friends, the World Calendar Association was incorporated and the first pamphlet *The World Calendar* was widely circulated. It was mailed immediately to the League of Nations and the two calendar committees which sponsored the thirteen-month plan. Editors of the Press and specialized lists were also included. The newly organized World Calendar Association was incorporated October 21 1930. As the preparatory committee of the League of Nations was scheduled for June 1931, something had to be done immediately to place the new time-plan in the forefront of action and to bring it to the attention of the League. Time was of necessity short, and every minute of the intervening eight months was precious.'

The minutes appear to have been well used, for when the following June came, Elisabeth Achelis was in Geneva to present her case, and in the meantime the first number had been produced, under the distinguished editorship of C. D. Morris, of the *Journal of Calendar Reform*, which has continued to appear quarterly ever since.

Miss Achelis's appearance before the League committee had been at least to some extent responsible for the square presentation, in the consequent Report, of the problem as it stood in 1931. Nor did her activities stop

THE WORLD CALENDAR

FIRST QUARTER

January

S	M	T	W	T	F	S
1	2	3	4	5	6	7
8	9	10	11	12	13	14
15	16	17	18	19	20	21
22	23	24	25	26	27	28
29	30	31				

February

S	M	T	W	T	F	S
				1	2	3	4
5	6	7	8	9	10	11
12	13	14	15	16	17	18
19	20	21	22	23	24	25
26	27	28	29	30		

March

S	M	T	W	T	F	S
					1	2
3	4	5	6	7	8	9
10	11	12	13	14	15	16
17	18	19	20	21	22	23
24	25	26	27	28	29	30

SECOND QUARTER

April

S	M	T	W	T	F	S
1	2	3	4	5	6	7
8	9	10	11	12	13	14
15	16	17	18	19	20	21
22	23	24	25	26	27	28
29	30	31				

May

S	M	T	W	T	F	S
				1	2	3	4
5	6	7	8	9	10	11
12	13	14	15	16	17	18
19	20	21	22	23	24	25
26	27	28	29	30		

June

S	M	T	W	T	F	S
					1	2
3	4	5	6	7	8	9
10	11	12	13	14	15	16
17	18	19	20	21	22	23
24	25	26	27	28	29	30W

THIRD QUARTER

July

S	M	T	W	T	F	S
1	2	3	4	5	6	7
8	9	10	11	12	13	14
15	16	17	18	19	20	21
22	23	24	25	26	27	28
29	30	31				

August

S	M	T	W	T	F	S
				1	2	3	4
5	6	7	8	9	10	11
12	13	14	15	16	17	18
19	20	21	22	23	24	25
26	27	28	29	30		

September

S	M	T	W	T	F	S
					1	2
3	4	5	6	7	8	9
10	11	12	13	14	15	16
17	18	19	20	21	22	23
24	25	26	27	28	29	30

FOURTH QUARTER

October

S	M	T	W	T	F	S
1	2	3	4	5	6	7
8	9	10	11	12	13	14
15	16	17	18	19	20	21
22	23	24	25	26	27	28
29	30	31				

November

S	M	T	W	T	F	S
				1	2	3	4
5	6	7	8	9	10	11
12	13	14	15	16	17	18
19	20	21	22	23	24	25
26	27	28	29	30		

December

S	M	T	W	T	F	S
					1	2
3	4	5	6	7	8	9
10	11	12	13	14	15	16
17	18	19	20	21	22	23
24	25	26	27	28	29	30W

Worldsday (a World Holiday), W or December 31 (365th day), follows December 30 every year. The Leap-year Day (another World Holiday), W or June 31 follows June 30 in leap years.

Every year is the same.

The quarters are equal: each quarter has exactly 91 days, 13 weeks or 3 months: the four quarters are identical in form.

Each month has 26 week-days, plus Sundays.

Each year begins on Sunday, January 1; each working year begins on Monday January 2.

Each quarter begins on Sunday, ends on Saturday.

The calendar is stabilized and perpetual, by ending the year with a 365th day that follows December 30 each year, called Worldsday dated 'W' or December 31, a year-end world holiday. Leap-year day is similarly added at the end of the second quarter, called Leap-year Day dated 'W' or June 31, another world holiday in leap years.

there. In an article in a later issue of the *Journal* summarizing the League of Nations calendar activities, Mrs. Key-Rasmussen, who had been a member of the League Secretariat, wrote: 'The World Calendar Association maintained and developed its activities and its President made new contacts and gained fresh support, especially among the Latin-American nations. In 1934, Miss Achelis visited eleven European countries in ten weeks and flew across the Ægean from Athens to Constantinople. Among the numerous persons she contacted in the Old World were influential civil and religious leaders. While in London, previous to the international conference in 1931, she met Mahatma Gandhi who in a signed statement, declared that he approved a perpetual calendar on a twelve-month basis, pointing out that as most Indian calendars were so arranged,[1] it would be easier of acceptance in his country.'

The next few years produced little but further discussion and argument. The Fourth General Conference of the League, for whose consideration so much preliminary work had been done, gave the Committee for Communications and Transit a vague mandate to 'follow the efforts which would doubtless continue to be made for the purpose of enlightening public opinion as to the advantages and disadvantages of a reform,' but for the rest placed the matter more or less on the shelf.

A significant development at this time was the marked diminution in the popularity of the Cotsworth thirteen-month calendar and conversely the apparently increased appreciation of the World Calendar. Two factors had contributed to this: the death in 1932 of Mr. George Eastman, who had been the principal financial support behind the International Fixed Calendar League: and the energetic proseletizing on its own behalf of the World Calendar Association. Very soon, so far as inter-

[1] See Part III, Chap. 5.

L

national consideration was concerned, the thirteen-month calendar had dropped out of the running; in the last round-up of the nations on the subject by the League in 1937, no vote was cast for the Cotsworth plan.[1] By then, the Association had the support of voluntary branches or 'affiliates' in several countries, and counted the number of chambers of commerce, rotary clubs, cultural societies, religious bodies, educational authorities, and similar organizations among its supporters, as well as eminent individuals, in hundreds.

This 1937 round-up of the nations, as I have called it, was the one definite objective step taken in the long-drawn-out investigation by the League which advanced the case. It arose out of a resolution passed by the International Labour Organization Congress at Santiago, Chile, in 1936, in favour of universal adoption of the World Calendar. The Chilean national calendar committee thereupon drafted a Convention and presented it to the League Council at its January 1937 meeting calling on member States to agree to the adoption of the 'perpetual calendar of twelve months and equal quarters and known as the World Calendar.' The Council referred the draft Convention and the Chilean resolution back to the Communications and Transit Committee, where it was sponsored by the Chilean Ambassador to Britain, H. E. Don Augustin Edwards. The proposed date for adoption of the new calendar was then January 1 1939, a date which, since it fell on a Sunday, would have made the transition from the old to the new systems a fairly simple matter. (It has since become obvious that the two years intervening would probably have proved a gravely inadequate period to cover preliminary arrangements such as printing and production of new calendars and almanacks, besides making no allowance

[1] Journal of Calendar Reform, 1942, p. 77.

for each nation's domestic legislation, but in the enthusiasm of the moment that angle was overlooked).

By March that year however, a copy of the Draft Convention had gone out to member governments—of whom there were in all 69. Forty-five replies were received by the League, although only 32 had come in when the Communications and Transit Committee met in September, and these responses were so mixed in their content that the Committee came to the decision not to come to a decision. It recorded its opinion that 'for the moment it is not opportune to contemplate the convocation of a Calendar Reform Conference which, in present circumstances, would not appear to have any prospect of achieving its object.'

That was the last official word on the subject by the League of Nations. It had done much good work. It had cleared the air, and cleared away the calendar debris. It had aligned the various countries into categories as supporters and non-supporters of reform. This was the way the nations lined up:

Definite approval of the World Calendar

Afghanistan	Greece	Peru	
Brazil	Hungary	Spain	
Chile	Mexico	Turkey	
China	Norway	Uruguay	
Esthonia	Panama		(14)

Opposing the World Calendar

Argentina	India	Rumania	
Haiti	Holland	Sweden	(6)

No observations to submit

Australia	Iraq	United States	
Denmark	Lichtenstein	Venezuela	
Iceland	Siam		(8)

Undecided

Bulgaria	Ecuador	Lithuania
Czechoslovakia	Finland	Switzerland
Egypt	Latvia	(10)

Reform considered premature—'Time not ripe'

Austria	New Zealand	South Africa
France	Poland	United Kingdom
Monaco		(7)

The political situation in many of these countries has of course completely changed since 1937. Some, too, who opposed it are known now to be strongly working for reform, e.g. India. In percentages, and in the now familiar Gallup language, the result was perhaps not too bad for a first attempt: It was:

For the World Calendar ..	31 per cent
Against the World Calendar	13 per cent
Don't know	56 per cent

No, not too bad!

CHAPTER VIII

Debate in Parliament

JUST AS Lord Desborough was during many years of his life the moving spirit behind the strong campaign for a fixed Easter voiced by the London and International Chambers of Commerce, so the late Rear-Admiral Beamish, R.N., devoted his later years to the general advocacy of calendar reform. He was greatly attracted by and a strong supporter of the World Calendar as the best proposal.

It was Admiral Beamish who, in 1944, stated the case for calendar reform in the House of Commons, putting it forward in a considered, logical and even learned address, only to have it 'talked out' with what must have been one of the silliest, most irrational and illogical effusions that even that House of many talks has heard.

The Admiral's speech was a model of concise and interesting, as well as entertaining information, and is worth quoting[1] not only because it brought the Parliamentary history of the calendar up-to-date at that time but also because it put frankly both sides of the case.

Rising on the Adjournment on Friday, March 17 1944, he opened with a revealing fact:

> From such research as I have been able to carry out it appears to me that it is 192 years since this House had a Debate upon calendar reform, and by calendar reform I mean a question of days and dates rather than the fixing of a religious festival.
>
> I may remark in passing that it took 170 years before we decided to have that Debate, so that things move slowly with

[1] Hansard, March 17 1944, Col. 633.

regard to calendar reform. I make no apology for raising this, and I speak on no one's behalf, at no one's request, and to no brief but my own. I make no apology because I feel that this is a matter very relevant to plans for reconstruction in pretty nearly every phase of our national life.

I presume that the House is very much aware of the type of calendar reform to which I propose to refer. At any rate I wish the fact that this idea of bringing in a rational calendar, as I would like to call it, should be in our records.

This rational calendar I wish to speak about has been described as a balanced, regular and perpetual calendar, and the present calendar of which we are also aware, and which muddles so many, is inconvenient, irregular, and a source of expense. It's defects, and it has many, are patent and certainly perpetual. I propose before I finish, and I wish to be as quick as I reasonably can, to put the points for and against the rational calendar which I have in mind.

At any rate the rational calendar is based on what we are all accustomed to, namely, the present or Gregorian calendar. To describe quite shortly the rational calendar, the twelve months we know so well remain: each quarter begins on Sunday and has three months, 13 weeks and 91 days; the same dates of the month will fall always on the same days of the week year after year, perpetually. In fact perhaps one of the most useful aspects of the rational calendar from the point of view of commerce, of business and in almost every other respect is the fact that each month will have 26 weekdays exclusive of Sundays. The first month in each quarter of the rational calendar always has 31 days and the other two months in each have 30, so that you have 31, 30, 30, in each of the successive quarters.

I may perhaps be allowed to remind the House that changes of this sort that are made from time to time take a good deal of time to carry into effect. 'Summer time' was certainly a British device, a pleasant convenience, an illogical interference with time and with fact. It took twenty years, if not more, to germinate. I would very respectfully say that the rational calendar of which I am now giving an outline causes very little interference indeed with the national life, and it certainly does not fly in the face of astronomical fact.

May I also remind the House that the Gregorian calendar which we now enjoy was the result of a decree passed in the year 1582 by Pope Gregory, and, as was not surprising at that time, the Protestant countries said it was a hopeless affair, a Popish calendar, and they would have nothing to do with it. Another fact of interest in the matter is that it is sixteen centuries, or round about sixteen centuries, since the Christian Emperor Constantine gave to us what we all so deeply revere and enjoy, the seven-day week. At any rate there is one thing about the seven-day week which we can usefully remember, that is, that it still retains the names of the pagan gods or of the sun and the planets, a nice mixture. At any rate the defects of the calendar we suffer from, and they really are genuine defects, are entirely due to the seven-day week and the 52-week-and-one-day year, and essentially to the odd day, making the calendar irregular, inconvenient and inconsistent. The odd day, as I say, is the cause of the anomalous and unnecessarily variable calendar, but it can be adjusted with quite a small measure of reason and goodwill. . . .

MR. DEPUTY-SPEAKER: I am sorry to interrupt, but a small measure of reason and goodwill would mean legislation, which is just where we must stop.

REAR-ADMIRAL BEAMISH: By the word 'measure' I did not mean a legislative measure: I really meant a small amount of good will.

MR. DEPUTY-SPEAKER: I do not see how that could alter the law.

REAR-ADMIRAL BEAMISH: I apologize if I was out of order. I have no intention of suggesting legislation. I am not sure that legislation would even be necessary in any way. I think this odd day could be adjusted. The proposal is for the odd day of the rational calendar to be fitted in between the 30th day of December and the first day of January, and it would have no date and no day of the week attached to it. We would call it any name we liked, and every country could have its own name for that particular day. It could be a Freedom Day or a Humanity Day, or a Brotherhood Day. Whatever it might be called, it certainly could, and should, be a universal holiday.

I know, of course, that when people speak of calendars they naturally think they ought to refer to the religious festivals.

I merely remark, in passing, that such a thing as the fixed Easter has been talked about for many centuries, and Martin Luther strongly advocated it. We have no necessity to complain about the accuracy of the Gregorian calendar because it will not let us in for serious trouble, amounting to only an odd day in the course of the next 3,000 years—and before that time we shall have a General Election, which will enable us to discuss it.

There are one or two other points of which I may remind the House, one of which I mentioned just now. It was not until 1752 that this House debated a reform of the calendar, and adopted the Gregorian calendar of 170 years before. Of course, the North American colonies of that time abided by our decision here. At any rate, it created a good deal of discussion. There was a rather ardent debate in the House, I believe, but I have not been able to see the record; and there were riots in the country. The people said 'We have been robbed of eleven days. We ought to be paid for them.' At any rate, all countries now use the Gregorian calendar, and they have all, without exception, noted its inconveniences, and the expense as well. I may mention some of its difficulties. There are four different lengths for the months—28, 29, 30 and 31 days. There are three different lengths for the quarters—90, 91 and 92 days. There are three different lengths for the half-years—181, 182 and 184 days. It seems to me that we should be freed of the absurd rhyme which one is always in trouble to remember.

I must mention Lord Desborough in this connection, because he raised this question in another place in 1932 and in 1936, but I think I am right in saying that it has never reached this House. We owe him a debt, because he and others have made a deep study of this matter, for which I, personally, am very grateful. The Fixed Easter Act, which is on the Statute Book, has, of course, some close link with the possibilities of an alteration in the calendar, but the question of an equal-quarter calendar, the calendar that I am now discussing, is not inseparably bound to that of a fixed Easter.

There is no logical reason why the English-speaking nations, and any other who like, should not adopt a fixed secular calendar, such as I am describing, leaving the Easter question for settlement by the Churches. I think that is an extremely important point—the most important point of all.   In the

United States there is a strong movement—which is as it should be at the present time—for this rational calendar, or world calendar as I believe they call it. They are much more active there than we have been here.

This, as I have said before, is not a new step. It was referred to the League of Nations in 1937. Forty-five nations were approached and given the fullest particulars of this rational[1] calendar. Six of them declared themselves against it. I am not able to give the names of the nations concerned. Fourteen said that they thought it an excellent idea and were in favour. The remainder were uncertain or silent, either because they did not know anything about it or because they thought it did not very much matter.

At any rate one interesting point emerged: the Vatican, to which we all owe a great debt for the Gregorian calendar, was not opposed. May I tell the House, in case anyone is inclined to suggest that we should be doing away with the beautiful old links with the past, that there is no need to feel any doubts on that score, because the rational calendar retains many of the old cherished associations and oddities of the Gregorian calendar, such as September, October, November and December, which are not, in fact, the seventh, eighth, ninth and tenth months of the year, as their names imply, but are, as we all know, the ninth, tenth, eleventh, and twelfth months. That is a cherished association. The other names are either numbers or are derived from Roman Emperors. Holidays come into the question. They present no serious difficulties. Religious festivals present difficulties that we all fully appreciate. I say that this rational calendar is primarily a commonsense calendar for all people.

Now I come to the prime difficulties that will face those who want to bring it in. First, the Orthodox Jews, who have a very complicated calendar of their own, will find considerable difficulty in accepting it, but no insuperable difficulty, and their official mouthpieces have made it clear that they would not put serious difficulties in the way of it. There are one or two religious organizations or sects who also find trouble in

[1] It should be noted that the 'rational' calendar to which Admiral Beamish was referring throughout was that known as the World Calendar.

accepting it. In particular I refer to the Seventh Day Adventists with whom I am not very familiar.

I just want to give a short idea of how I think the Minister and the Home Office should proceed in order to popularize and publicize this suggestion that I am putting out. I hope that he will find it simple to circularize chambers of commerce, local authorities, chambers of trade, trade unions, banks, High Commissioners for the Dominions, Colonial representatives, and last, but by no means least, the British Broadcasting Corporation. Then there is the Astronomical Society, the Meteorological Society, the Statistical Society, and in particular, the most important of all from the point of view of expense and bother, the Incorporated Society of Chartered Accountants and Auditors.

I may safely say that in almost every phase of national life the rational calendar will bring simplicity and comfort. The first Tuesday after the first Monday in October, for instance, will become an unchanging date, instead of a cumbrous expression. In finance, Government and education, it will help. In statistics and in accountancy, which I think are of very great importance, comparisons from being odious and anomalous, as they are now, certainly so far as trade and commerce are concerned, will become seductive and consistent.

My last word is to remind the House that there are certain convenient dates when the present calendar fits in with the proposal for a rational calendar. They are not immediate, nor are they very frequent. The first one is January 1st, 1945, the next one July 1st, 1945, the next is March 1st, 1946, and the next January 1st, 1950. The present calendar and the proposed calendar meet on those dates and it would be a great mistake to introduce the rational calendar unless the calendars did meet as I say.

So I just want to wind up by saying to the Minister that I beg him to be a little bit enthusiastic about this after a little more study. I feel confident that he will agree with what I have tried to say, and that he will take all possible action in preparation for international agreement about this, which is essential, and the first thing is to make quite sure that everybody in all our home circles and in business are acquainted with the details of the plan.

Thus eloquently the gallant Admiral presented the case. He had put forward a reasoned and reasonable argument for reform. What happened? Let us continue the story as it is recorded in Hansard:

MR. AUSTIN HOPKINSON (Moseley): If I might take a moment or two I should like to express my disapproval and disagreement with what has fallen from the hon. and gallant Member. Surely, in these days, to suggest that a thing is good because it is rational is to attempt to dam back the whole spirit of this age and put back the clock. The spirit of this age is irrationality in all human activities—the revolt and reaction against the rationality of the nineteenth century.

We see it in art, for example. Anyone studying modern sculpture and painting must agree, that the chief object of the leaders of modernism in art is to divorce rationality of any sort from the particular art which they practise. We see it also in the case of literature, in the works of Mr. James Joyce,[1] for example, and other writers who are gradually producing a formless literature which has no meaning of any sort or kind but is simply a jingle of words. We see it perhaps at its best in some of our modern poetry, where rationality is taboo altogether. There is in it no reason, no rhythm and no rhyme, nor anything at all, except a mass of words, disconnected from one another, and intended not to please the reader or the hearer, but to show what an extraordinarily clever person the writer is.

REAR-ADMIRAL BEAMISH: Do I understand the hon. Member to suggest that anything which is rational is retrograde?

MR. HOPKINSON: It is, most certainly. It is against the whole spirit of the age. The whole spirit of the age is against reason of every sort. I gave the example of art and literature. Let me turn to economics. The new idea in economics is divorced from reason of every sort. It is based, as Lord Keynes has told us many times, upon the principle that it is possible to get a quart out of a pint pot, and that it is also possible—and the

[1] The Irish writer, not to be confused with James Avery Joyce, English barrister and keen advocate of calendar reform, now Hon. Secretary of the British Section of the World Calendar Association.

Labour Party have this as the basis of their economic system—to eat your cake and have it tomorrow. I venture to suggest that that is a revolt against the hidebound rationalism of the nineteenth century and the Manchester School of Economics.

We get the same thing in religion. In the Roman Empire, at the time when it was breaking up—as ours appears to be at the present time—a great mass of superstition overcame Rome. The old gods disappeared and every sort of superstition took their place: astralism, the cult of Magna Mater, of Isis, of Serapis, and so on, just as is happening now with us. In such things as the Oxford Group, you have a perfect example of the effect of irrationalism in religion.

In politics also, we observe the revolt against rationalism and reason of any sort is rapidly being stimulated. Our Parliamentary system now consists of a Labour Party, which is a small minority of this House forming the Government of the country and also forming the Opposition in this House. That is the triumph of irrationality in politics. I stand almost alone in this nation today in putting forward the view that irrationality is not a sound basis for human activity. But my point is that the hon. and gallant Gentleman is trying to stem the current of modern thought and modern idealism which is entirely irrational.

REAR-ADMIRAL BEAMISH: My hon. Friend is preventing the Front Bench from giving me a reply.

MR. HOPKINSON: There is a sort of criminal flavour about this whole Debate; otherwise why is the representative of the Home Secretary here to answer? I must repeat that to introduce rationalism into our country would be entirely against the spirit of the whole age, against the spirit of this House in particular, and against the spirit of the Labour Party perhaps even more.

There are two other points, with one of which I agree and the other I disagree. The hon. and gallant Member thinks there might be some difficulty in getting rid of the extra day; but I understand that in Scotland that difficulty has been completely solved and that the bulk of the population in Scotland after 24 hours, have no recollection of one particular day of the year, a day not very far from 1st January. That day each year is a blank in the memory of all Scotsmen, and, if the same system were introduced into England, we would get over the difficulty which the hon. and gallant Member raised.

MR. MATHERS: Is the hon. Member aware that now he is descending from being merely facetious, and apparently clever, to being absolutely foolish?

MR. HOPKINSON: The hon. Member should have said 'rational'. I am glad he appreciates my point of view. The other point I wish to raise is: Why on earth did the hon. and gallant Member introduce the Emperor Constantine into this? He pointed out that the Emperor Constantine preserved the names of the old gods in his calendar. Of course the reason is this, as a little consideration will show him. The Emperor Constantine was, of all men, a hedger. He was hedging the whole time, and history relates that although he made Christianity the official religion of his Empire, he himself very carefully refrained from being baptised until just before his death. My history is a little vague but I think I am right in saying that only twenty years before he adopted Christianity as the official religion, he had published an edict adopting Mithraism as the official religion and therefore, as an authority upon what is proper and right, the Emperor Constantine might be left out of the argument.

After these absurdities, Mr. Hopkinson's effort to talk the subject out seems to have failed him, and he sat down, giving at last an opportunity for a Government statement on the matter, for which all the supporters of reform had long been waiting. Mr. Peake, Under-Secretary for the Home Office, rose:

I was most conscious, as I am sure you were, Mr. Deputy-Speaker, of the difficulty in which my hon. and gallant friend found himself, in raising the subject of calendar reform upon the Adjournment, because our calendar depends upon the Acts of 1750 and 1751, associated with the name of Lord Chesterfield, which produced the riots in London to which my hon. and gallant Friend referred. My hon. and gallant Friend, therefore, had to confine himself, so far as he could, to criticisms of our present calendar, rather than the merit of his own alternative.

My hon. Friend below the Gangway was not hampered in that way because, so far as I could see, his speech had very little to do with the subject of calendar reform. In the two minutes that are left to me, I can only say that the necessary conditions under which the reform of our calendar could be undertaken do not exist at the present time.

For any steps in this direction, it would be necessary to have the concordance of all the Christian Churches. Many Churches would object very strongly to any interference with the succession of seventh days as our Sundays, and having one week every year with eight days in it. Moreover, there are other religious bodies, which are interested in this question of the seventh day. . . .

Here the irrepressible Hopkinson broke in again to demand, 'Could the right hon. gentleman tell us about the Seventh Day Adventists?' He received no reply, and the Under-Secretary continued.

MR. PEAKE: You would require also international agreement. Our Acts of 1750 and 1751 were introduced because our calendar was out of gear with that in use throughout the civilized world, and it is perfectly clear that you must have agreement between the great majority of civilized countries, before any calendar reform can be introduced. In the last place, you must have a substantial measure of public opinion in this country in favour of making the change. The calendar which my hon. and gallant Friend has in mind—it is only one of 500 different kinds of calendar reform which have been suggested, but is I think the best of them all—would, in fact, abolish four of our present days in the year and thereby deprive, in my calculation, approximately 500,000 people of their birthdays, and those people might have something to say about it.

I congratulate my hon. and gallant Friend on being able to bring this subject forward, but there is a great deal more work to be done before the time is ripe for change.

There, then, was the official point of view, but there was still a minute or so left for debate. Now Mr. Ivor

Thomas, Member for Keighley, rose to take advantage of the opportunity to have the last word.

> MR. IVOR THOMAS: I hope the Minister will not overlook one grave defect of this scheme, in which every person would have the same day for his birthday every year. It is bad enough to be born on April 1, but to have one's birthday always on a Monday would be perfectly intolerable. There is also the great historical objection. As I represent the traditional party which has suggested this before, may I as a member of the revolutionary party hope that we shall not destroy the precious links with Numa, Gregory XIII and Julius Cæsar which we have in our present calendar——

At this point Hansard records, in its usual cold italic type:

> *It being the hour appointed for the Adjournment of the House, Mr. Deputy-Speaker adjourned the House without Question put, pursuant to the Standard Order.*

Thus, in mid-air, ended the first serious presentation of the calendar case (as distinguished from Easter) before the House of Commons for more than a century and a half. It had almost failed to get a hearing at all, and when it did the time available for discussion was mostly wasted by inconsequent opposition which, whether it was intended as raillery or obstruction, was patently absurd and uninformed.

But it did produce a Government statement.

At this time also the war was still raging and the outcome not decided. Moreover, the whole of that day and the preceding day in the House had been spent in heated debate of a still more controversial question: the establishment of a national health service (realized two years later). Therefore it was an achievement on the part of Admiral Beamish to have brought forward at all a subject which to many members concerned and troubled by such portentous affairs must have seemed slight and intangible. And the Home Office reply proved revealing.

It revealed that the Government, as such, had no opposition to offer to a reformed calendar. At the same time it pointed out three areas where opposition might lie—first, with the Christian Churches (although this has proved largely non-existent particularly when Easter is separated from the cause); second, with other religious bodies—notably the Jews and Seventh Day Adventists, whose objection had anyway been mentioned by Admiral Beamish; and third, by the traditionalists who would object to change on principle and who might feel aggrieved because their birthday dates were inconvenienced.

Most importantly, however, it revealed the Government's attitude in the words: 'you must have a substantial measure of public opinion in this country in favour of making the change', and in Mr. Peake's final sentence when he said: '. . . but there is a great deal more work to be done before the time is ripe for change'.

It revealed that the Government was not and would not be prepared to act until public demand compelled it. That had been the official attitude in 1937 when in reply to the direct question of the League of Nations the British Government had been among those who had answered in almost the same words that 'the time was not ripe'; it was so in 1944; and it is much the same today.

When, one wonders, will the time be ripe?

PART III

CHAPTER I

The Statisticians Speak

OF ALL THE SCIENCES troubled with such inconsistencies as those of the calendar, one would expect that
of Statistics to be most concerned, for Statistics is by
definition the collection and arrangement of facts and
figures in relation to quantity and time. In Britain the
Royal Statistical Society, a learned body, has given the
subject some attention, but beyond a general exploration
has not pursued it to a conclusion or firm recommendation; in the United States the American Statistical
Society has dealt with it by producing an interesting but
somewhat complex series of mathematical tables which
are mainly of value to the actuary, the accountant and
the industrialist. In France, the Associacion de Normalisation and in Geneva, the International Organization
for Standardization, both have the subject under consideration as this is written, and are actively engaged in
collecting and collating the views of their associated
bodies on the solution of the calendar problem.

It was in 1934 that in London the Royal Statistical
Society set up a Committee made up of six of its members to go carefully into the question and 'to give serious
consideration to the proposals for calendar reform', but
long before that date aspects of the question had come up
for debate at the Society's meetings. Most notable of
these occasions was on the reading of a Paper in May
1925, 'The Week or Month as an Intermediate Time-
unit for Statistical Purposes',[1] by Sir Napier Shaw,
Sc.D., F.R.S., who was at that time head of the British
Government's meteorological services.

Dr. Shaw explained his reasons for introducing the

[1] Royal Statistical Society Proc., Vol. 88.

subject for discussion at that time. Two circumstances, he said, had led to it. The first was that the Chief of the U.S. Weather Bureau had announced that the Bureau was in possession of fifty years of weather observations and wished to decide on the best method of grouping these for statistical purposes and presenting the conclusions; the second that the British Ministry of Agriculture had recently taken up the systematic correlation of weather conditions with agricultural and horticultural procedure. The American Chief of the Weather Bureau, Dr. Marvin, favoured the employment of the week of seven days, extended to eight days for one week (two weeks in leap years) and grouping the weeks into fortnights or 'months' of four weeks; the British solution had emerged as a system of collecting information from stations month by month, but meterological data for districts week by week.

Thus, said Dr. Shaw, 'on both sides of the Atlantic we are confronted with the rival claims of the week and the month as the intermediate unit of time between the day and the year for statistical purposes, and the subject is sufficiently important for statisticians to give some attention to it.'

At this time the League of Nations had recently begun its consideration of the subject, and there was this fact also to take into account from the statistician's point of view. 'It would be something of a catastrophe for the League of Nations in its cosmopolitan wisdom to arrange a reform of the calendar and to learn afterwards that the requirements of statistical sciences pointed to something quite different; and such a catastrophe is really not unlikely, and for a curious reason, and that is the incompatibility and irreconcilability of the month and the week. . . . The whole subject is full of incongruities.' However, it should be noted that when Sir Napier Shaw was advancing this opinion the World Calendar proposal had not yet emerged; that was not destined to appear on the scene as such for League consideration until 1930.

We are led to understand [he went on] that all statistical presentations of observed facts which are concerned with a succession of periods of time must embody at least two principles: a principle of measurement, and a principle of adjustment for the purpose of reconciliation. It is no exaggeration to say that the statistical method is in its essence a method of comparison of data at different times for different places, or for different classes of facts; consequently, it is of the highest importance that statisticians should agree not only upon the principles of measurement but also upon the principle of adjustment.

There is, so far as I know, no difference of opinion as to regarding the day as a primary unit in the principle of measurement, and there is complete accord in regarding the hour, the minute and the second as accepted sub-divisions of the primary unit. I refer to the unanimity with some sadness, because for modern methods of computation they are really barbarous divisions of the day. Next to the day, the year is the most generally accepted unit, but the unanimity is to some extent affected by divergence of opinion as to the principle of adjustment. Generally speaking, we are agreed that a year consists of 365 days with an adjustment for leap year, but for some statistics the principle of adjustment makes the year generally 364 days (52 weeks) with an occasional year of 371 days (53 weeks).

The week and the month are, as I have said, fundamentally irreconcilable, but they take on a specious appearance of reconciliation in the quarters, which may be of thirteen weeks including 91 days, or three months of 90, 91 or 92 days.

He gave then a few appropriate figures to show the hopelessness of finding a common devisor: the lunar month, which has an average duration of 29·530588715 days; the solar year of 365·2422166 days;[1] our calendar year of 365 or 366, and our calendar months of 28, 29, 30 or 31 days. 'As far as keeping in touch with successive new moons our months are an egregious failure,' said Dr. Shaw, and added: 'It is rather remarkable that it

[1] The Astronomer Royal has given the length of the mean tropical year as 365·242199 days.

should ever have been accepted, and we may wonder what degree of compulsion was exercised to enforce the acceptance of the beginning of the calendar month as a substitute for the visible sign of the new moon for the payment of periodic instalments of rent and interest.'

Then the speaker made the point which is the basis of the whole problem. '*The principle of the reconciliation of the month with the year as expounded by our Calendar is frankly no reconciliation at all*,' he said. '*And yet it is the basis of innumerable statistics*.' To show the lack of unanimity in methods of keeping long-term statistics in relation to various activities he then put forward some tables, of which the following are an abbreviation:

TABLE 1

Principles of division and accompanying principles of adjustment.
Principles of Statistical Practice.

Category	Principle of Division	Principle of Adjustment
A	5-day periods	One 6-day period in leap year
B	7-day periods (weeks)	One 8-day week in an ordinary year; two 8-day weeks in leap years
C	7-day periods (weeks)	52-week with occasional 53-week leap year.
D	10-day periods (decades)	11 days or 8 days in final period of the month; 9 days in final period in leap-year.
E	28–31-day months	29-day month in leap year.
F	Quarters of 13 weeks each.	52- or 53-week year, as 'C'.
G	Quarters of the civil year of 3 months each.	As in 'E'.
H	Quarters of the farmers' year (3 months beginning with September)	As in 'E'.
I	Quarters of the 'May year' centred at equinox and solstice	As in 'B'.
Z	Whole period of 365 days	366 days in leap year.

A — Agricultural   F — Financial   M—Meteorological
R — Railway   S — Social   T — Trades and Shipping
V — Vital statistics

TABLE 2[1]

Categories selected for various classes of statistics in various countries

Denmark ..	..	(V)	C (Sats.)
Egypt ..	..	(V)	C (Wed.)
Strasbourg ..	..	(M)	A E
Germany ..	..	(V)	C (Sat.)
Great Britain	..	(A)	C Z
		(F)	Z (Mar. 31)
		(M)	A C (St.) E F Z
		(R)	E G Z

Separate statistics in (V) and (A) class for Scotland, England and
Wales and Ireland, were also mainly divided as 'C' category.

Greece ..	..	(M)	A D E
Holland ..	..	(M)	D E
Italy ..	..	(M)	D E
Portugal ..	..	(M)	D E
Azores ..	..	(M)	D E
Laurenco Marques ..	..	(M)	D E
Spain ..	..	(V)	C (Wed.)
Sweden ..	..	(M)	E H
Switzerland ..	..	(V)	C (Sat.)
U.S.A. ..	..	(A)	C (Tues., Fri., Sat.) E
		(M)	C (from Jan. 1) E
		(V)	C (Sat.) Z

All the rest of the countries shown (about 50) used the general E or Z
for (apparently) all purposes.

Having discussed this extraordinary multiplicity of
methods, and 'in view of the divergences of practice,'
Dr. Shaw expressed the opinion (speaking of course as a
statistican) that 'the time has arrived when those who
are interested in the formation of effective tables of
statistics should formulate some opinion on the questions
at issue,' and submitted the following suggestions:

(1) That the reconciliation between the sub-period
and the year should be accomplished within each year
in turn, and not delayed for completion for a four- or
five-year period;

[1] Abridged.

(2) That no reconciliation between the week and the month is possible;

(3) That the consensus of opinion respecting 'climate and crops', as well as vital statistics, is that a shorter period than a calendar month is necessary.

(4) That, in view of the fact that the adjustment of months to the year fails to keep the months in touch with the actual phases of the moon, and is at best imperfect, the division of the year into twelve more or less equal parts *cannot be regarded as a fundamental principle of statistical science*.

These views he then proceeded to elaborate somewhat, and there followed a learned discussion, but no effective conclusion resulted beyond the meteorologist's enunciation that he found 'something attractive about using the broad brush of a quarter to paint the statistical picture of seasonal variations', and that our present quarters are not the best since 'they make bad shots at the equinoxes and solstices'. He preferred the ecclesiastical quarters ending on Lady Day, Midsummer Day, Michaelmas and Christmas Day, or, better still, the quarters of the 'May year' centred on the equinoxes and solstices, which are 'adumbrated by the Scottish quarter-days (Candlemas, Whitsuntide, Lammas, and Martinmas), as giving the best summary of the sun's influence'. However, the Rev. Theodore Phillips, who in the debate summarized the work of the League of Nations to date—as Secretary of the Royal Astronomical Society he had been chosen by the Archbishop of Canterbury to be his representative on the League's Committee considering the Calendar—deprecated Dr. Shaw's 'ecclesiastical quarters', as, he said, 'he would have thought them to be hopelessly impractical from a statistical point of view. They consisted of 91, 97, 87 and 90 days respectively'.

It cannot be said that even so eminent a scientist as Sir Napier Shaw had advanced the prospect of an easy solution of the complex calendar problem. The irreconcilable periods were still irreconcilable. In fact, the suggestion he had made in his Point Four that the twelve-month division of the year 'could not be regarded as a fundamental principle of statistical science' seemed rather to set the clock back. The old stumbling block of the incommensurability of the year and the month took on an extra corner for reformers to stumble over. And what is perhaps more surprising is that not a vestige of a way out was suggested. And, be it noted particularly, no reference was made to the thirteen-month calendar idea as a possible alternative.

Yet there are no other ways. If the year is to be divided into 'months' at all there must be either twelve or thirteen. Not even the five-day and six-day weeks experimented with in the U.S.S.R. or the ten-day week of the French revolutionary calendar—and these are surely the most daring calendar experiments within practical competence—have eliminated the 'month'. Each kind of week could still be (and was) grouped into a 30-day month.

The weakness of the 13-month plan we have discussed elsewhere (see page 145). As for the twelve-month it is difficult to agree that provided the months are given a regular sequence, such as the World Calendar's 31, 30, 30, repeating perpetually, this does not provide a sound statistical basis for records, meteorological or others. Even the exceptional days (Worldsday and Leapday) would provide a regular pattern, rhythmical and symmetrical, as compared with the irregular sequences of months, varying almost haphazardly between 28 and 31 days, of the present calendar.

However, the R.S.S. left the subject thus in the air in 1925. Nine years later, on July 11 1934, they approached it again, this time to form a Committee seriously to study it, on the grounds that 'H.M. Government will be called upon, at a Conference of the League of Nations early in 1935, to give its opinion about the two proposed schemes

176   TIME COUNTS

(twelve months and thirteen months) and it is still "un-advised" on the statistical aspect, on which no other body but the Society is competent to advise it'.

Now, it is seen, the twelve-month and the thirteen-month issue had squarely to be faced.

The committee consisted of six men of science, all eminent in their own fields: Dr. L. Isserlis (chairman), Messrs. R. L. Connor, R. C. Glendar, J. Leak, and Dr. E. C. Rhodes, and finally Sir Napier Shaw, although unfortunately, Dr. Shaw was at this time too unwell to attend the several meetings which were held.

In due course their conclusions were submitted 'for the information and consideration of the Council',[1] and although some of these conclusions are somewhat remarkable they are important in that they represent the considered opinion of the appointed representatives of the most eminent learned body which has undertaken a serious investigation of the subject in Britain. The following were the principal points:

(b) The existing calendar presents real difficulties in statistical work both in comparison of statistical material within the year and in comparisons from year to year;

(c) Some of these difficulties will be removed by the fixation of Easter . . . [but] when the 1928 Easter Act is put into operation, the difficulties will not be entirely removed. Easter cannot be 'fixed' unless the calendar is such that the days of the week fall on the same days of the month in all years;

(e) Quarterly statistics are essential in the case of the data of economics and commerce. This consideration appears to rule out completely the year of thirteen months. . .;

(f) It is desirable that the year should have a fixed distribution of week-days, i.e. that November 26th for example, should fall on the same day of the week every year.

(g) Agricultural and meteorological phenomena are so closely related to the sequence of the solar year that it is essential that the time scale should keep in step with the mean solar

[1] *Journal of the Royal Statistical Society*, Vol. 98.

year of 365·2422 days. It follows if the calendar is to be used as a time-scale that devices equivalent to those of the Gregorian Calendar must be retained. If therefore, desideratum (f) is to be attained (and with it a definitely fixed Easter) 'extra' days or 'extra' weeks will have to be introduced. The Rational Calendar Association[1] suggest four quarters each consisting of three months, the first 31 days and the other two months 30 days; the year ending with a *dies non* termed 'New Year's Eve' and containing also in Gregorian leap years a second *dies non* termed 'leap day' after June 30th.

(h) The calendar suggested by the R.C.A. has merits but cannot be accepted as a definite solution. The one or two intercalary days can be made

    (i) to take the place of existing Bank Holidays,

    (ii) additional Bank Holidays, or

    (iii) (especially the extra day at the end of the year) a day devoted to stocktaking, balancing of books, and so forth.

A difficulty will arise, however, which though not statistical in character, cannot be overlooked. Religious bodies may attach very great importance to the regular sequence of Sundays.

(i) This difficulty does not arise if the intercalation consisted of complete weeks, so that some years contained 52 weeks and other 53. The Gregorian Calendar provides for 97 leap years in 400 years, i.e., 400 periods of 364 days (equal to 52 weeks) each and 497 additional days (equal to 71 additional weeks).

LUSTRA

A calendar could therefore be arranged in lustra; the first four years of each lustrum would be ordinary years of 52 weeks each, and the fifth year a leapyear of 53 weeks; the last year of every tenth Lustrum would, however, be an ordinary year.

This would give nine leap years of 53 weeks every 50 years and 72 leap years every 400 years; a further correction would

[1] The Rational Calendar Association was the name adopted by a Parliamentary group formed in London in 1931 to support a campaign for the adoption of the World Calendar. (See "The English Story", Part 3, Chap. vi.)

therefore be required by which the 175th or 225th year would be an ordinary year as well as the 200th.

This would of course tend to create difficulties in the case of yearly and quarterly comparisons, since every five or six years would occur a year with 2 per cent more weeks than normal, and a quarter of 98 days instead of 91, 7 per cent more than normal.

Finally the Committee recommended that 'bodies dealing with calendar reform should give careful consideration to the suggestion in the preceding paragraph'.

Thus the British statisticians officially left the subject not very much clearer than it had seemed in the discussion nine years earlier. They had indeed ruled out the thirteen-month proposal, but without supporting the twelve-month alternative. And they had introduced a new idea of their own which served only to increase the complexities of the problem by adding one more possibility to the scores which the League of Nations had already considered. The lustra principle was not in itself new; it had occurred in a number of the proposals submitted to the League. Nor does there seem to be a worth-while purpose in substituting for the present irregular calendar—whose vagaries are at least familiar—another which merely switched the irregularities of months into irregularities of years. While the desirable advantage of perpetuity in beginning every new year on the same day of the week would be attained, and there would be useful groups of four consecutive years in which all vagaries had been eliminated, the 5th and 50th years, not to mention the widely spaced 175th and 225th would call for exceptional treatment, and thus themselves form new variations.

It is difficult to see that the advantages would outweigh the disadvantages, and one is left with the thought that this solution, in Hamlet's words:

puzzles the will
And makes us rather bear those ills we have,
Than fly to others that we know not of.

This is not, however, entirely to disparage a genuine attempt to find a solution from a strictly scientific point of view. The answer lies no doubt in the fact that there is no ideal solution, since the measures of the weeks, the lunar months and the quarters are incommensurable. Only the partition of time into days and eras provides the exact divisional figures required for perfection; and one might go a step further than this and say that only the system employed by astronomers of counting the days in a continuous numerical sequence from the arbitrarily selected date of January 1, B.C. 4713 (noon), provides us with a scientifically irrefutable and translatable date. By that measure January 1 1956, instead of being so called, will be the 2,335,472nd day. The size of this number is, to say the least, inconvenient. In the same way though in a lesser degree, the system of numbering the days through a single year has proved inconvenient, although it is a system which has always been obvious and available, as by calling February 1 the 32nd day and continuing this numeration through the year. (This would not, in any case, remove the inconvenience of particular date numbers falling on different days of the week.)

The American Approach

The American Statistical Association, counterpart in the United States of the Royal Statistical Society in England, have also given thought to the calendar, but whereas the British organization has confined itself to theory and overall recommendation, the American body has gone further and analyzed the calendar's inconsistencies in an imposing set of tables. No more impressive indictment of the present calendar's failure to meet the needs of industrial statistics could well be devised than the table of 'calendar shift indexes for various relative values of Saturday and Sunday' later described, and reproduced in page 183.

While it would seem that the R.S.S. had primarily in mind the meteorological and agricultural aspects of the subject, which admittedly are tremendously important, the A.S.A. appears characteristically to have devoted its attention more sharply to the no less essential industrial angle. The result has been the provision of adequate tables which by a simple (or not so simple) mathematical procedure permit the 'smoothing-out' of the ragged time-data inevitably due to our varying month-lengths and irregularly-spaced general holidays.

Although the Association has considered the problem over a long time and from a number of different angles, its most useful study has undoubtedly been that which deals with monthly comparison, affecting production, distribution and calculation in many forms and infinite applications. No more valuable contribution to the science of statistics could be made than that by Mr. Charles E. Armstrong, published in the Association's Journal,[1] dealing with statistical adjustment for calendar irregularities. The Armstrong method sets out to provide an exact comparison of any one month against an 'average' month, particularly as applied to production in industry, and its complexity is yet another witness to the inadequacy of the Gregorian calendar to modern industrial needs. This is demonstrated in the application of the method to time-analysis where Saturdays and Sundays are required to be included.

In series of monthly data in which the contributions of Saturdays and Sundays to the monthly totals are different from those of weekdays, explains the author, variations in the number of Saturdays or Sundays in a month produce corresponding fluctuations of monthly data. Since our calendar shifts two days in leap years and one day in all other years, the number of Saturdays and Sundays in any given month usually changes from

[1] *The American Statistician* (American Statistical Association, Washington, D.C.), October-December, 1950.

one year to the next. For example, January had four
Saturdays and four Sundays in 1947, five Saturdays
and four Sundays in 1948, five Saturdays and five
Sundays in 1949, and four Saturdays and five Sundays
in 1950.

Though at first sight startling, this example is not so
unusual as might be expected, for any 30-day or 31-day
month can have similar variations in different years.
Where either a Saturday or a Sunday, or both, require
to be considered as parts of a day, the calculations
become complicated. If, for instance, Saturday is equal
to 0·7 of a weekday or full working-day, and Sunday
equals 0·3, a four-Saturday, five-Sunday January would
contain $(4 \times 0·7) + (5 \times 0·3) + 22 = 26·3$ equivalent
working days. Dividing the January total by this figure
would put the data on an equivalent day basis, and
repeating the procedure for all months covered would
eliminate the effects of calendar shift. Thus there can
be eight, nine, or ten fractions to add to the number of
week-days in any month according to the month-
pattern, and if these are correctly calculated a sound
standard of comparison for month to month is available.

By adding, in any particular case, a series of twelve
months of equivalent days obtained in this way, a useful
average monthly figure over one year is provided for
general comparison with an individual month. This,
however, ignores holidays and seasonal variations.

For more exact analysis the Armstrong system pro-
ceeds to establish an index figure based on percentage in
which the average of 30-day and 31-day months, counting Saturday and Sunday as full equivalent days, is 100.
Then an ordinary (non-leap year) February has an index
99·12, and, *excepting only leap-Februaries*, a month of
any Saturday-Sunday pattern, and with any equivalent-
day value for either or both of these days, can be given
an accurate index figure. The following is the Armstrong
formula:

Let a month with four Saturdays and four Sundays be an a-month; with five Saturdays and four Sundays a b-month; with four Saturdays and five Sundays a c-month; and five Saturdays and five Sundays a d-month. Then

Index for an a-month

$$= 100 \times \frac{4 \text{ Sa} + 4 \text{ Su} + 22 \cdot 66}{4 \cdot 38 \text{ Sa} - 4 \cdot 38 \text{ Su} - 21 \cdot 90}$$

Index for a b-month

$$= 100 \times \frac{5 \text{ Sa} + 4 \text{ Su} + 21 \cdot 66}{4 \cdot 38 \text{ Sa} - 4 \cdot 38 \text{ Su} - 21 \cdot 90}$$

Index for a c-month

$$= 100 \times \frac{4 \text{ Sa} + 4 \text{ Su} + 21 \cdot 66}{4 \cdot 38 \text{ Sa} - 4 \cdot 38 \text{ Su} - 21 \cdot 90}$$

Index for a d-month

$$= 100 \times \frac{5 \text{ Sa} + 5 \text{ Su} + 20 \cdot 66}{4 \cdot 38 \text{ Sa} - 4 \cdot 38 \text{ Su} - 21 \cdot 90}$$

where Sa represents the proportionate part of a week-day represented by a Saturday, and Su the proportionate part represented by a Sunday. These equations give monthly percentage figures for all months except February, which required special treatment, particularly in leap years. For February, the appropriate equations are:

(1) Non-leap year index = 99·1
(2) Leap year 'a' index = 102·7 + 0·155 (a—d)
(3) Leap year 'b' index = 102·7 + 0·155 (a—d)—1·085 (a—b)
(4) Leap year 'c' index = 102·7 + 0·155 (a—d)—1·085 (a—c)

In this way it is possible to obtain equivalent values of working time for all months.

Dividing the data by the index-figures thus arrived at places the original monthly data on an equated

TABLE OF COMPARATIVE MONTHS

The Armstrong Index

Calendar shift indexes for various relative values of
Saturday and Sunday[1]

Percent of Week-day		Indexes for all Non-February Months				Basic Indexes for Leap-Year Februarys[2]		
Saturday	Sunday	a	b	c	d	a	b	c
			READ	DOWN				
100	100	100·00	100·00	100·00	100·00	102·65+	102·65+	102·65+
100	80	100·25+	100·25+	99·58	99·58	102·75	102·75	102·02
100	60	100·53	100·53	99·14	99·14	102·87	102·87	101·36
100	50	100·67	100·67	98·91	98·91	102·92	102·92	101·01
100	40	100·81	100·81	98·67	98·67	102·98	102·98	100·66
100	20	101·12	101·12	98·17	98·17	103·11	103·11	99·91
100	0	101·45−	101·45−	97·64	97·64	103·24	103·24	99·12
80	80	100·53	99·83	99·83	99·14	102·87	102·11	102·11
80	60	100·81	100·10	99·39	98·67	102·98	102·21	101·44
80	50	100·96	100·24	99·15+	98·43	103·04	102·26	101·08
80	40	101·12	100·38	91·00	98·17	103·11	102·31	100·71
80	20	101·45−	100·68	98·40	97·64	103·24	102·40	99·93
80	0	101·79	101·01	97·86	97·07	103·38	102·53	99·12
60	60	101·12	99·65−	99·65−	98·17	103·11	101·52	101·52
60	50	101·28	99·78	99·41	97·91	103·17	101·54	101·14
60	40	101·45−	99·92	99·16	97·64	103·24	101·58	100·76
60	20	101·79	100·22−	98·65−	97·07	103·38	101·68	99·97
60	0	102·17	100·54	98·09	96·46	103·54	101·77	99·12
50	50	101·45−	99·54	99·54	97·64	103·24	101·17	101·17
50	40	101·62	99·68	99·30	97·36	103·31	101·21	100·79
50	20	101·98	99·98	98·77	96·77	103·46	101·29	99·98
50	0	102·37	100·29	98·22	96·14	103·62	101·36	99·12
40	40	101·79	99·43	99·43	97·07	103·38	100·82	100·82
40	20	102·17	99·72	98·91	96·46	103·54	100·88	100·00
40	0	102·57	100·03	98·34	95·81	103·70	100·94	99·12
20	20	102·57	99·19	99·19	95·81−	103·70	100·03	100·03
20	0	103·00	99·49	98·61	95·10	103·87	100·06	99·12
0	0	103·47	98·90	98·90	94·34	104·07	99·12	99·12
Sunday	Saturday	a	c	b	d	a	c	b

READ UP

[1] From *Journal of Calendar Reform*, March 1951.

[2] All non-leap-year February indexes are 99·12. The arrangement of the table follows that used in trigonometric tables, and by avoiding duplicate listings, shortens the table considerably.

monthly basis, which assumes all 31-day months contain $\frac{31}{7} = 4.43$ equivalent weeks, and all 30-day months contain $\frac{30}{7} = 4.29$ equivalent weeks. For any given set of values of Saturdays and Sunday there are only seven possible calendar shift indexes, but no allowance is made for seasonal variations. Using the indexes given, for various combinations of whole and fractional values of Saturdays and Sundays, the Table on page 183 is obtained. For other fractional values, simple interpolation can be used, or the indexes may be worked out using the above equations.[1]

[2] For further mathematical procedures in this interesting system the reader is referred to *The American Statistician*, October-December 1950 (American Statistical Association, 1603 K St., Washington 6) or *Journal of Calendar Reform*, March 1951 (World Calendar Association, International Building, 630 Fifth Avenue, New York 20).

CHAPTER II

Practical Uses

SOME DAY THERE may be undertaken by someone
with unlimited time at his own disposal a statistical
estimate of how much money, energy and time might
be saved by the introduction of a calendar with regular
months, following in regular quarterly sequence. Its
value for business comparisons, as for one month compared with another, or one quarter with the preceding
quarter, is plain; add to that the further convenience of
having the years themselves made comparable, one
against another, by the steadying of the wandering
holidays, and we have an immense saving.

To get at just how much expenditure of time and
money would be saved is not easy. It is one of those
vague things that defy exactitude. Nor, strangely
enough, will those who might be expected to benefit
most, always co-operate most readily. Indeed, often
enough they will not co-operate at all, even in finding
out. 'We have not the time', they say. So precise data is
not available, though there have been published from
time to time round estimates of likely results of reform,
such as the suggestion made by a leading Canadian
advertising agent in a speech on calendar reform in
Toronto that 'the very least estimate is that enough
money could be saved under the World Calendar to
provide every agency in the country with another man,
free of charge', and a statement by Mr. Joseph M. Naab,
a president of the American National Association of
Cost Accountants, that 'it is estimated that calendar
reform will enable American business men to effect

savings annually sufficient to pay the interest on the national debt'.[1]

These are generalizations, and it is possible to arrive at somewhat closer estimates than they suggest. With a view to getting down to figures in at least one industry the present writer recently investigated as a sample the case of a group of retail shops in the men's outfitting and haberdashery trade in Britain. The result was revealing.

According to the last official returns[2] there are in Britain 14,587 men's wear shops, selling men's and boys' clothes, shirts, haberdashery and sundry articles of masculine attire. They employ 66,749 men and women, who receive in wages and salaries £17,043,000. Of these, 8,011 are one-man businesses and others grouped in chains of anything from two or three to fifty or more retail establishments. Some of the larger of these have their own factories, making many of the items sold in their shops.

The firm under examination was one of these, with a headquarters office and store in London and some seventy retail shops scattered throughout the large towns. They had also their own factories in which such articles as shirts and ties were made. It was once a private, now a public company, with a capital exceeding two millions. Its book-keeping system had expanded with the business, from small beginnings, but had been thoroughly modernized, and its accountancy was in charge of a secretary and assistant secretary, both chartered accountants. The activities of such a business are dependent very largely on a seasonal trade, as are of course most businesses concerned with textile productions, whether retail or manufacturing. This was both. On its retail side moreover it was particularly susceptible to the incidence of public holidays.

[1] *Journal of Calendar Reform*, Vol. XXI, p. 17.
[2] Board of Trade figures.

It was early in the new year that the present author discussed with one of the accountants of this firm the problems that arose directly out of calendar irregularities. The time was still near enough to the preceding Christmas for this particular period to be fresh in his mind.

'With Christmas falling on a Thursday last year',[1] he said, 'we had three shopping days during the actual Christmas week against only one the previous year, when it fell on a Tuesday. Consequently, comparison of the takings figures to see how our sales compared in the two years for the three weeks or so before the holiday (and for that portion of the month) was no easy task. It could be most misleading in view of the facts that (a) December 1951 began on a Saturday, and in 1952 on a Monday, which gave the two Decembers different patterns, and (b) there were two extra shopping days in 1952 in the Christmas week itself.

'To help to overcome this last difficulty and to make comparisons of any value to us, we found it necessary to ignore fluctuations between 1951's and 1952's corresponding Christmas week totals, and to compare instead the *five*-weekly period beginning on the Mondays three complete weeks before Christmas and finishing at the end of the week which includes New Year's Day.

'The inclusion of the New Year in this period is necessary to us as the period from Christmas to the New Year can be a busy one on the retail side, especially for branches which remain open on Boxing Day (as in Scotland) or close on New Year's Day, e.g., Glasgow, Edinburgh, Darlington, Sunderland, Manchester, etc. In our own case it is necessary also because the takings of the day finish (for book-keeping purposes) at midday, and the carry-forward of Christmas Eve therefore goes into the New Year's total.

'Every year a similar problem arises. The only comparisons that can be made with any fairness must cover

[1] 1952, a leap year.

a wider period than the precise Christmas weeks, because they are never of the same pattern in two consecutive years. If, however, Christmas day were fixed to fall on a particular day (whichever day of the week it might be), then comparison with corresponding weeks or months or previous years would present no difficulty whatever. This would hold good for all periods of the year too, of course. What a boon to accountants that would be'.

Although the question of Easter is regarded as outside that of calendar reform in general, it is very much a part of the problem for the textile trade. 'Another difficulty we come across', this accountant continued, 'is that with Easter and Whitsuntide floating as they now do through the months of March to June inclusive,[1] sales during this period are affected so considerably that comparison of the *monthly pattern of trade* during these four calendar months is practically valueless. A fixed Easter, combined with a symmetrical calendar, would however cure this so easily. The wandering of Christmas over the seven days of the week, and Easter and Whitsun over four months of the year, create a serious and inevitable problem for accountants'. He agreed that such adjustments occupied much time, and ought not to be necessary. With a sensible calendar they would not be.

The next subject discussed was costing. 'From this point of view', he said 'a fixed calendar would be a tremendous asset. The break-down of a firm's trading year into twelve calendar months for costing, statistical and other allied purposes leads at present to all manner of difficulties due to the different number of working days in the months. We, like many other firms, use for these purposes "4-weekly" periods. It is a method that overcomes the difficulty of the number of working days, but presents other troubles in the form of apportionment of those numerous costs and expenses which are

[1] See diagram, page 126.

paid or incurred monthly, quarterly or yearly'. Sooner or later also, he pointed out, some adjustment such as a 27-week 'half-year' or at least a five-week month is called for to reconcile the four-weekly month periods with the calendar months.

As an example, he then mentioned a stock-taking and cost analysis with which he had just had to deal in his own firm. 'On the one hand, for our published Balance Sheet and Accounts', he explained, 'our trading year ends on January 31, a date which was selected as coinciding with the 'quietest' time from the retail point of view. The January sales have ended and stocks are at their lowest. On the other hand, we close our books at the factories, and take stock there, twice a year, as nearly as possible to the calendar year and half-year dates, i.e., at the end of June and December, the close of the natural business half-years for the factories, when their stocks too are at their lowest.

'When either of these periods ends on a Saturday or a Sunday that is quite simple; we have merely to work out the figures for the previous twenty-six weeks. When however, as last year, December 31 falls on a Wednesday —bang in the middle of the week—it is a different matter. We must choose either the previous week-end or the one following, and make such apportionments of the monthly, quarterly and half-yearly charges and over-heads as are necessary.

'In the case I have just dealt with, for the second half of the year, we decided to take the 27-week period ending January 3 1953. It did not lend itself to easy apportion-ments, but for our own domestic purposes it was the most convenient as the factories were closed for the Christmas period—and it made the most useful com-parison in our own case with the previous year.

'The amount of extra work entailed in arriving at exact costing over this 27-week period can easily be imagined. It required apportionment of salaries of monthly paid staff over 27 fifty-secondths of their annual salary, for example, and in the same way 27 fifty-secondths of such charges as insurances, rents, rates and land-tax, and light, heating and water charges which are ordinarily calculated quarterly, half-yearly, or annually, but could only be correctly estimated by taking special meter-readings.

'It all took a great deal of time—and all directly due to the vagaries of our calendar. With years, half-years and quarter-years that ended on the same days of the week as the same periods in the previous year, or, better still, invariably at the week-ends (as does the World Calendar) all this tricky and extra work would have been quite unnecessary'.

'And what proportion of your time did it take?' I asked, 'Some hours?'

'Yes, some hours, certainly'.

'Would it be reasonable to suggest that calendar adjustments—these and others throughout the year—absorb, say, two or three per cent of the accountant's or book-keeper's time in this type of business, or even five, or say ten per cent?'

'I don't know. It's impossible to work out a thing like that, but at a guess I would say that it's not far short of five per cent'.

'Not far short of five per cent'. Out of this rough but authoritative estimate we can begin to deduce the cost of calendar incongruities to the country's retail business. As we have seen, the men's wear trade alone employs 66,748 men and women. It would be not unfair (as our accountant friend agreed) to estimate that at least one in twenty—or five per cent—were employed as book-keepers, ledger clerks, or accountants. Of the total wages figure of £17,043,000 therefore, a sum of about £850,000 is spent on book-keeping. Five per cent of this figure is £42,500.

We may reasonably say, therefore, that the faults—so

easily corrected—of the Gregorian calendar cost the men's wear trade alone something like £42,500 a year.

There are scores of trades in which the same sort of analysis would no doubt produce a comparable result. And this takes account only of time wasted in superfluous book-keeping and accountancy; the indirect losses caused through wandering holidays are probably much greater.

For another view of the wastefulness in time and energy of the present calendar the writer is indebted to an industrial consultant, Mr. S. J. Noel-Brown, head of a firm of business management consultants whose experience covers a considerable range of enterprises.

Such an organization, it should be explained for any reader unfamiliar with this comparatively new and not-very-well-known profession of management consultancy, is called on to probe and analyse, as well as to report upon the production, procedure, administration and accountancy of such firms as may call on it for expert advice. It necessarily obtains therefore an overall view of business activity and efficiency in various branches of industry which could be got in no other way. For this reason, the opinion of an experienced consultant can be regarded as that of an expert in industry.

First dealt with in this instance was the question of standard costing, a modern system developed by production executives and accountants over the last few years for precise analysis of pre-production costs. It supersedes the traditional method of working out an 'average' cost of a particular item of production over an extended period of time; it permits analysis to an extremely fine point and is described as a development of the modern movement towards more scientific works costing in relation to time, the governing factor in all production problems. It was shown how, in standard costing, an improved calendar, such as the World Calendar, would simplify accountancy operations.

In standard costing, then, in order accurately to appor-
tion annual expenditure over respective months of varying lengths, it is necessary first to determine the weeks
in a standard month as follows:

Days in year: 365

Weeks in year: $\dfrac{365}{7} = 52\cdot1428571$

Weeks in standard month (one twelfth of year):

$\dfrac{52\cdot1428571}{12} = 4\cdot345238$

Thus the standard cost for a 28-day month =
   $4\cdot345238 \times 4 \times$ standard cost for standard month
   = standard cost for standard month $\times$ 0·920547948
For a 30-day month the standard cost would be:
   standard cost for standard month $\times$ 0·986301325;
For a 31-day month the standard cost would be:
   standard cost for standard month $\times$ 1·019178741

This is a very cumbersome procedure, by no means
simplified if Sundays and the whole or part of Saturday
(or any other weekday) are excluded from the calculations.

With the World Calendar in use and so with each
month having 26 working days, it would be possible to
divide annual expenditure into twelve equal parts with
an assurance of accuracy. A slight complication would
ensue if the cost had to be spread over Monday to
Friday inclusive as in this case there would be 22 working
days for eight of the months, and 21 only for four months.

Perhaps the most important implication from the
point of view of standard costing is that with the World
Calendar each Quarter is identical. At present, whatever
periods are selected for comparison, there are discrepancies in the actual number of days. Even 13
periods of 28 days leave one day unaccounted for—and
though some firms have been driven to use this method,
it is artificial and complicated inasmuch as it is necessary
to prepare a special calendar so that such expressions as
'period 8, week 3' can be understood.

The most commonly used system is probably what is known as 4-4-5, that is to say, two four-week months are followed by one five-week month. Whatever day of the week is chosen from which to start or finish the so-called 'month' it rarely tallies with the existing calendar. For instance, referring to Table 1, it will be noted that there are eight cases throughout the year where the present calendar follows the cycle 4-4-5. These are:

Mondays: 1st and 2nd Quarters;

Tuesdays: All four Quarters;

Wednesdays: 4th Quarter;

Sundays: 1st Quarter.

Incidentally, it will be seen that there are only 12 Wednesdays in the 1st Quarter, but 14 in the 3rd Quarter; while there are also 14 Thursdays in the 4th Quarter. Any system involving allocation of costs which starts or finishes on a Thursday, takes place 53 times during the year instead of 52. With the World Calendar, each day would occur 52 times throughout the year and any day would be as good as any other day as the start or finish of a costing period, and comparable figures, monthly, or yearly, would readily be obtained.

TABLE 1

Number of times specific days recur within specific months in 1953.

	Mon.	Tues.	Wed.	Thur.	Fri.	Sat.	Sun.
January	4	4	4 ⎫	5	5	5	4
February	4	4	4 ⎬12	4	4	4	4
March	5	5	4 ⎭	4	4	4	5
April	4	4	5	5	4	4	4
May	4	4	4	4	5	5	5
June	5	5	4	4	4	4	4
July	4	4	5 ⎫	5	5	4	4
August	5	4	4 ⎬14	4	4	5	5
September	4	5	5 ⎭	4	4	4	4
October	4	4	4	5 ⎫	5	5	4
November	5	4	4	4 ⎬14	4	4	5
December	4	5	5	5 ⎭	4	4	4

This applies also, of course, to the apportionment of actual or expected expenses for estimating, budgetary control, or any other purpose calling for comparison or financial allocation.

Another defect of the present calendar is that there are a varying number of working days to the various months and this causes difficulty when planning production, making delivery promises, arranging procurement schedules, machine lading, and similar operations. For instance, as will be noted from Table 2, on a five-day working week, the number of working days per month varies from 20 to 23, on a five and a half-day week from 22 to 25 and on a six-day week from 24 to 27. These are considerable deviations and where output per machine hour or per operator hour is standard, the volume of production during the month varies in direct proportion to the figures quoted.

TABLE 2

Number of working days for month (excluding deductions for holidays).

	5-day Week (Mon.-Fri.)	5½-day Week (Mon.-Fri. plus half Sat.)	6-day Week (Mon.-Sat.)
January	22	24½	27
February	20	22	24
March	22	24	26
April	22	24	26
May	21	23½	26
June	22	24	26
July	23	25	27
August	21	23½	26
September	22	24	26
October	22	24½	27
November	21	23	25
December	23	25	27

This has yet another implication. In many industries it is customary to have a monthly production target or pay a monthly bonus. If, when the number of working days in the month are fewer, the target is allowed to remain the same, the percentage achievement will probably be less and workpeople will be disgruntled. If the target is reduced the operatives may think that less effort is required, and the target may not then be reached.

The most striking illustration of the complications of the present calendar is obtained when production plans, delivery schedules or machine loads are prepared graphically on a Gantt or similar chart. Undoubtedly, more widespread use of visual graphs and charts is one of the benefits of modern planning prevented by the complexities arising out of the variations in the number of working days contained in the present months. The present calendar also causes considerable difficulties in the case of long-term planning of, say, aircraft programmes, civil engineering contracts and the like. Calendars are normally available only one year ahead, and often others must be specially prepared to meet planning in excess of that period. To meet this situation the firm had to prepare for their own use a complete calendar covering the years from 1901 to 1999.[1]

This calendar, due to the Noel-Brown organization is an interesting illustration of the complications set up by the varying patterns of a non-perpetual calendar. At the same time it offers a comparatively quick method of ascertaining the day of the week for any date within the 99-year period. For example, to find the day of the week for March 31 1962, find the year in the block on the top left-hand side, then follow the arrow to the right till you come to the letter 'D' under March. Reference to Table 'D' shows that March 31 1962 will fall on a Saturday. Conversely, to find when Christmas Day will next fall on a Sunday, first note the Table on which the 25th is shown as a Sunday (Table 'D') and then look under the column 'December' for 'D', and read off the year (1956) on the left.

[1] See next page.

1901 TO 1999 CALENDAR

	JAN.	FEB.	MAR.	APR.	MAY	JUN.	JUL.	AUG.	SEP.	OCT.	NOV.	DEC.
	B	E	E	A	C	F	A	D	G	B	E	G
	C	F	F	B	D	G	B	E	A	C	F	A
	D	G	G	C	E	A	C	F	B	D	G	B
	G	C	C	F	A	D	F	B	E	G	C	E
	A	D	D	G	B	E	G	C	F	A	D	F
	E	A	A	D	F	B	D	G	C	E	A	C
	F	B	B	E	G	C	E	A	D	F	B	D

1901	1907	1918	1929	1935	1946	1957	1963	1974	1985	1991
1902	1913	1919	1930	1941	1947	1958	1969	1975	1986	1997
1903	1914	1925	1931	1942	1953	1959	1970	1981	1987	1998
1905	1911	1922	1933	1939	1950	1961	1967	1978	1989	1995
1906	1917	1923	1934	1945	1951	1962	1973	1979	1990	....
1909	1915	1926	1937	1943	1954	1965	1971	1982	1993	1999
1910	1921	1927	1938	1949	1955	1966	1977	1983	1994	....

LEAP YEARS:

	JAN.	FEB.	MAR.	APR.	MAY	JUN.	JUL.	AUG.	SEP.	OCT.	NOV.	DEC.
	D	G	A	D	F	B	D	G	C	E	A	C
	B	E	F	B	D	G	B	E	A	C	F	A
	G	C	D	G	B	E	G	C	F	A	D	F
	E	A	B	E	G	C	E	A	D	F	B	D
	C	F	G	C	E	A	C	F	B	D	G	B
	A	D	E	A	C	F	A	D	G	B	E	G
	F	B	C	F	A	D	F	B	E	G	C	E

1904	1932	1960	1988
1908	1936	1964	1992
1912	1940	1968	1996
1916	1944	1972	....
1920	1948	1976	....
1924	1952	1980	....
1928	1956	1984	....

A

S	M	T	W	T	F	S
		1	2	3	4	5
6	7	8	9	10	11	12
13	14	15	16	17	18	19
20	21	22	23	24	25	26
27	28	29	30	31		

B

S	M	T	W	T	F	S
			1	2	3	4
5	6	7	8	9	10	11
12	13	14	15	16	17	18
19	20	21	22	23	24	25
26	27	28	29	30	31	

C

S	M	T	W	T	F	S
				1	2	3
4	5	6	7	8	9	10
11	12	13	14	15	16	17
18	19	20	21	22	23	24
25	26	27	28	29	30	31

D

S	M	T	W	T	F	S
					1	2
3	4	5	6	7	8	9
10	11	12	13	14	15	16
17	18	19	20	21	22	23
24	25	26	27	28	29	30
31						

E

S	M	T	W	T	F	S
						1
2	3	4	5	6	7	8
9	10	11	12	13	14	15
16	17	18	19	20	21	22
23	24	25	26	27	28	29
30	31					

F

S	M	T	W	T	F	S
1	2	3	4	5	6	7
8	9	10	11	12	13	14
15	16	17	18	19	20	21
22	23	24	25	26	27	28
29	30	31				

G

S	M	T	W	T	F	S
1	2	3	4	5	6	
7	8	9	10	11	12	13
14	15	16	17	18	19	20
21	22	23	24	25	26	27
28	29	30	31			

Ninety-nine-year Calendar. For particulars of how to use to find the day of the week for any Gregorian date from January 1, 1901 to December 31, 1999, see page 195.

This calendar, moreover, provides an illuminating contrast to the simple World Calendar for one Quarter (see below) which, being completely repetitive for all time, provides at a glance all the information required.

Succinctly, Noel-Brown sums up: 'In my view, and that of my firm as industrial management consultants, covering a very wide experience of many industries and branches of commerce and involving work on all aspects of administration, costing and production, adoption of the World Calendar would greatly simplify planning, costing and many other activities and permit greater accuracy of control information, and therefore greater efficiency'.

THE WORLD CALENDAR

January April July October							February May August November							March June September December						
S	M	T	W	T	F	S	S	M	T	W	T	F	S	S	M	T	W	T	F	S
1	2	3	4	5	6	7					1	2	3	4						1	2
8	9	10	11	12	13	14	5	6	7	8	9	10	11	3	4	5	6	7	8	9
15	16	17	18	19	20	21	12	13	14	15	16	17	18	10	11	12	13	14	15	16
22	23	24	25	26	27	28	19	20	21	22	23	24	25	17	18	19	20	21	22	33
29	30	31					26	27	28	29	30			24	25	26	27	28	29	30 W

W=Extra-calendrical Worldsday at end of December, and Leapyear Day at end of June in leap years.

CHAPTER III

The Opposition

WHEN THE ROYAL Statistical Society's calendar committee submitted to its members its suggestions for consideration, it referred to 'a difficulty . . . which, though not statistical in character, cannot be overlooked. Religious bodies may attach very great importance to the regular sequence of Sundays'.

The same point was made by Lord Merthyr when, in December 1952, he addressed the Royal Society of Arts in London on the subject of 'a reformed calendar', and dealt specifically with the World Calendar.

'I should be foolish', he said, 'if I attempted to hide the fact that there are objections to the World Calendar. One of the reasons for the reluctance of people to adopt it is no doubt mere apathy, which many reformers have found is one of the most difficult obstacles to overcome. Another is tradition. There will I suppose be thousands of people who will oppose this change as they oppose all others, merely because it is a change; but there are also objections which carry weight, which are put forward by authoritative sources, and which deserve analysis and invite argument. The main objection is a religious one'.

We have seen how religious prejudice held up the adoption of the Gregorian calendar in England for 170 years between 1582 and 1752, and long after that religious feelings were exploited to keep up opposition to the reform for political ends. It is on record that when Bradley, the Astronomer Royal who had taken an important part in bringing about the reform, was sinking

under mortal disease, 'many people ascribed his suffer-
ings to a judgment from heaven for having taken part in
the "impious undertaking" '.[1]

In these broader-minded days bigotry is happily not
so rampant, and religious leaders at least give wise and
careful thought to modern needs within the bounds of
their faiths. So it has been with the modern calendar
movement, which, in fact, originated in the mind of, or
at least was first formally publicized by a Roman
Catholic priest, the Abbé Mastrofini, in 1834. As long
ago as 1912, in reply to an inquiry sent to the Vatican by
the International Congress of Chambers of Commerce
held in Boston, the following dictum was received: 'The
Holy See declared that it made no objection but invited
the civil powers to enter into an accord on the reform of
the civil calendar, after which it would willingly grant
its collaboration in so far as the matter affected religious
feasts'.[1] Nothing more definite has since been stated,
but it is clear that the Church is principally concerned
with the question of Easter and the festivals depending
on it, as is the case also with the Anglican Church; a
position which was made clear when the Easter Act
1928 was passed, and became subject to agreement
between all the Christian faiths. Innumerable clerics of
all denominations have not only agreed with the principle
of, but actively supported, calendar reform.

But there are exceptions. From the beginning of the
movement for the adoption of reform by the use of the
stabilizing or extra-calendrical 365th day—the only
practical way of making the calendar perpetual—
orthodox Jews have set themselves strongly against it, as
have the Seventh Day Adventists, the latter a religious
sect more populous and influential in the United States
than in Britain. More recently there has aligned itself

[1] Justin McCarthy, *History of the Four Georges* (1912, p. 509).

[2] *The Calendar for Everybody*, p. 68 quoting *The Catholic News*
(U.S.A.), March 27 1937, and *Journal of Calendar Reform*, Vol. 7, p. 85.

with these objectors the Lord's Day Observance Society, an energetic and voluble organization pledged to defend the sanctity of the English Sunday.

All of these make the same objection: that the introduction of the intercalary day in any week of the year, making, in effect, an eight-day week, breaks the sequence of the Sundays, or Sabbaths, and 'is contrary to divine law'.

It is a germane objection, and where it is held it is no doubt very sincerely held. But its strength as an objection, and also its weakness, are both contained in the assumption of the words 'divine law'. To accept it, one must accept—as these objectors accept without controversy—that the creation of the seven-day week was 'divine'. That it is one of the oldest features of the known early calendars is undoubtedly the case, but scholars are not agreed on its earliest use. Alexander Philip says that 'the seven-day week is of Semitic origin. Traces of it are to be found among Chaldean, Egyptian and even Greek records. Indeed among many peoples the number seven seems to have been endowed with peculiar significance. But it was among the Jews that the seven-day week was fully developed, and it is from them that its observance has spread over, and now so largely dominates, the civilized world.

'Whether it represents the special value and veneration attached to the number seven or has reference to the number of the planets or of notes in the musical scale, or whether it is a rude attempt at a quarterly division of the lunar month cannot now be ascertained, although the idea that it had any reference to lunar phases is negatived by the fact that the number seven and periods of seven are so frequently used in Jewish law in cases where there was no connection with the lunar month. According to Jewish tradition it was instituted at the creation, the successive states of which it was believed to symbolize. Its observance, having been neglected, was revived while the children of Israel were journeying through the wilderness'.[1]

The same authority held that 'in the widespread Mongolian or Turcanian race described by Isaac Taylor as "the ethnological substratum of the whole world". and with which we should probably associate the megalithic remains so extensively distributed throughout the world, there are evident traces of the early observance of a five-day week. A week of five days was also observed among what ethnologists now describe as the Nordic Race—the race which inhabited the lands surrounding the Baltic, and by whom rather than by Teutonic inhabitants of central Europe it is now well established that the British Isles were largely colonized. . . . The names of our weekdays make it clear that this five-day week at one time prevailed in Britain. No doubt the missionaries of Christianity were responsible for the introduction of the seven-day week . . .'.

Thus it would seem that the five-day division of time can be traced as far, and even farther back than the seven-day. Not all religious authorities hold the principle of the stabilizing days, with their necessary incidental eight-day weeks to be an insurmountable obstacle to otherwise desirable reform. Illuminative evidence was obtained on this point in 1934 by an authority which could hardly be biased on the subject—the United Press of America—who issued a questionnaire to ministers of various denominations throughout the United States, and among a total of 1,178 replies, received 907 in favour of the World Calendar and 131 in favour of the then more prominent thirteen-months calendar, both of which call for the extra calendrical year-end and leap-year days.[2] In the same year, *The Sign*, the American national Catholic magazine, printed a learned article by

[1] Alexander Philip, *The Calendar: Its History, Structure and Improvement* (Cambridge University Press, 1921).

[2] *Journal of Calendar Reform*, Vol. 14, p. 126.

Dr. E. S. Schwegler, a Roman Catholic priest of Buffalo, N.Y., in which he listed the numerous Roman Catholic ecclesiastics who had propounded various schemes for calendar reform many of which embodied this intercalary-day principle for the purpose of achieving perpetuity.

Moreover, in spite of the strenuous opposition which has been offered to the reform on the part of those Jewish leaders who were invited to put forward their views during the long investigation of the problem by the League of Nations, not all Jews oppose it. Dr. Julian Morgenstern, President Emeritus of Hebrew Union College, Cincinnati, Ohio, has stated: 'Should our Government ever officially recognize the civil World Calendar, American Jews would accept this calendar readily and apply it for civil purposes. It would then become their responsibility to find a way to harmonize their traditional religious observances with the new and now official calendar'.[1] It is interesting also that in 'an unofficial poll, taken by an interested delegation (of the United Nations), of information direct from chancelleries and delegations reveals the following attitudes on the World Calendar resolution (then before the United Nations)': and listing 47 countries as 'favourable', one of these countries is Israel.

However, what remains probably the best reply to the opposition on this controversial question of the unbroken cycle of the week was made by Dr. Charles F. Marvin, a member of the U.S. delegation to the Organization for Communications and Transit of the League of Nations at its fourth General Conference in October 1931. Dr. Marvin asked that the following statement should be recorded as an appendix to the Minutes of the Conference, and it was so recorded.[2]

[1] From a pamphlet, *Religion and the World Calendar* (World Calendar Association).

[2] League of Nations Document No. C.977. M.542. 1931. VIII.

Dr. Charles F. Marvin's Statement

If it can be shown that the cycle of the week has been broken even once, then it is inconsistent to raise any religious protest against breaking it again.

In what follows, any reader will see that the weekly cycle has been broken, not only once, but many times. These breaks have not occurred in connection with a world change in the calendar, because only one change has been made since the week became a part of national calendars. The breaks do occur, however, simply for man's convenience in the use of any calendar under natural conditions of life, as will be more fully explained presently.

Case No. 1: Early Christians—In the first place, it is well known that Jesus Christ's disciples and followers were all Jews, and many Jews became Christians; also that the early Christians soon left off observing the seventh day as a holy day, and shifted to the observance of the first day of the week as Sunday instead. Each such change from worship on Saturday to worship on Sunday involved an eight-day week once for each individual who made such a change.

These are bona fide cases in which, for purely religious reasons, devout Bible believers fully justified themselves in breaking the cycle of the week.

Case No. 2: Purchase of Alaska—Coming down through the ages, history again supplies a still more striking case in which a whole population again broke the cycle of the week purely as a calendar adjustment, purely as a matter of man-made convenience for harmoniously reckoning time. Many now living can remember when Alaska was purchased by the United States of America from Russia in 1867. At that time, its whole population used the Russian—that is, the Old Julian—calendar. Dates by this calendar were then twelve days later than the corresponding dates in the Gregorian calendar used by the United States. Accordingly, after the acquisition by the United States, these twelve days had to be dropped out; just as Pope Gregory dropped out ten days in 1582; just as England and the American colonies dropped out eleven days in 1752. So the whole population of Alaska in 1867 had to drop out twelve dates from its local calendar, and did so, but without breaking the cycle of the week.

Strangely enough, however, even this did not bring the Alaska Calendar into harmony as regards exact dates and week-day-names with the calendar used by the citizens of British North America, California and all the rest of the United States. Before the change, Alaskan days and dates were those of the Eastern Hemisphere—but, after the change, Alaskan week-days and dates had to harmonize with those of the Western Hemisphere.

Figuratively speaking, Alaska had crossed the 180th Meridian, the International Date Line. A week-day name and one extra date had to be added. In effect their new calendar had to start out with one eight-day week and the cycle of the week was then broken and has remained broken ever since.

It is futile to try to explain away the insertion of that eighth day in the week as an incident like crossing the International Date Line, on the ground of travelling around the world and setting back our watches three hours when we travel from New York to San Francisco, etc. These diversions of thought on the part of certain Sabbatarian writers are mere smoke-screens to hide the troublesome truth, or to mislead the uninformed.

In the process of this change of the calendar in Alaska, none of the population made any changes in its clocks, no one travelled or circumnavigated the globe, least of all Alaska itself, nevertheless the whole population put one eight-day week in its new calendar.

This is a bona fide Case No. 2, in which the cycle of the week has been broken to harmonize the calendar-reckoning with man's idea of what the calendar should be. Can anyone say that to consent to this kind of a calendar-adjustment in the last week of each year is a wilful violation of God's fourth Commandment?

Case No. 3. *The International Date Line.* Even to many well-informed people, especially those not accustomed to frequently traversing the Pacific Ocean, the adding and dropping of days and dates on crossing the 180th Meridian is a mystifying and curious question. Let me try to clarify the matter.

First of all, it is one more relatively modern, man-devised artifice or arbitrary convention to preserve harmony of calendars in different parts of the world.

The International Date Line is an imaginary line running from the North Pole to the South Pole, down the Pacific Ocean. Throughout most of its course it follows exactly the 180th Meridian of longitude. It is a purely imaginary, arbitrary man-devized convention for separating the calendar of the Eastern Hemisphere from that of the Western Hemisphere. For reasons which we shall try to make clear presently, and whether man likes it that way or not, nature makes these calendars perpetually differ from each other by just one day.

Where the 180th Meridian passes over any land area, or over or between the Aleutian and South-Pacific islands, the Date line is diverted to a course that runs over water areas, so as not to divide areas or islands belonging to the same nation. This diverted course, however, never differs very much from the 180th Meridian.

When the sun rises on the International Date Line a new day of light dawns, but it is not the same calendar day and date on opposite sides of the line. Here is where the Eastern Hemisphere joins the Western Hemisphere. Here is where yesterday ends and to-morrow begins. At the one single fleeting instant of midnight only, it is today on both sides of the line. For one single fleeting instant, paradoxical as it may seem, A.M. and P.M. of today co-exist simultaneously side by side. At the next instant, tomorrow is born, where P.M. of today was, and throughout the extent of this date line two consecutive calendar days and dates co-exist perpetually side by side.

If it is Sunday in the Eastern Hemisphere, then it is Saturday in the Western Hemisphere except as explained, at the single fleeting instant of midnight on the line. Two calendar days and dates co-exist here perpetually. Citizens of the islands lying closely contiguous to the date line often cross it, and in doing so must add or drop a day and a date from their calendar. No journey around the world, or any extended part of such a journey, is requisite to become involved in this calendar perplexity.

It is easy to speculate upon the enormous increase the future is certain to bring in the intermingling of citizens of the Eastern and Western Hemispheres, with the extension of populations westwards and the advent of flying from island to island, and from continent to continent. No one can take his old Sabbath with him, whether his religious traditions justify him or not. Nature simply compels him to break the cycle of his week, or become a nonconformist with his co-worshippers.

Among the people of the future, the occurrence of both eight-day as well as six-day weeks will thereby become a commonplace event. How can a small number of ultra-orthodox religious leaders hope to explain away their inconsistency in accepting the calendar adjustment at the date line, and opposing the year-day and leap-day? Consistency compels them to accept both or reject both.

The condition that the International Date Line separates the calendar of the Eastern Hemisphere from that of the Western Hemisphere, and that these two calendars perpetually differ by one day, are facts and conditions of Nature.

Every traveller crossing this date line (literally, he need only step across it) from the Orient must live through two consecutive calendar dates, dates which bear the same weekday name. To such a person, the Decalogue Sabbaths are separated by an interval of eight days. He has broken the cycle of the week. The cycle is always broken by everyone, whether he crosses from the Orient or the Occident.

This practice is simply a modern man-arranged expedient which nature imposes in order to preserve harmony and order in our calendar, as long as we live on a world revolving on its axis and illuminated by a sun. Without this arbitrary adjustment, hopeless confusion would soon prevail in this present age of extensive intermingling of eastern and western citizens who chance to cross the date line. Each such traveller would otherwise carry to his destination his own calendar week-day names and dates, in conflict with the reckoning of the community in which he settled.

Moreover, the whole adjustment has been unobtrusively introduced and is now universally accepted and practised as a matter of course by all. Not a voice is ever heard from the most super-conscientious Bible believer. Not a voice is raised to say that these six or eight-day weeks, coming daily into hundreds of lives, constitute a violation of God's fourth Commandment.

Here again history, reason and common sense bring us face to face with hundreds of cases of broken cycles. No arguments or explanations can change the facts. Eastern and western calendars along the International Date Line perpetually differ by one day. No one can cross the line from one zone to the other, either way, without a real break in the weekly cycle. No voice is raised to stop or prevent this calendar adjustment, on the ground that it involves a violation of the fourth Commandment, or any other law of God.

Is it not, therefore, grossly inconsistent for the Jewish and Sabbatarian leaders to accept the man-made calendar adjustment on the date line, and so vigorously oppose the same kind of calendar adjustment by the use of year-day and leapday?

Let us show how analogous the two adjustments are:

At the instant of midnight, between every December 31st and January 1st, the earth starts out upon its mighty annual journey around the sun. Whether man likes it or not, it returns to the same point in its orbit after fifty-two seven-day weeks, plus one day and a fraction. In order to simplify our present inconvenient calendar, the proposal is made that the fifty-second week of each annual journey around the sun consists of the customary seven days plus one day bearing a non-weekday name.

It is impossible to take up annually the fraction of a day, so this fraction is allowed to accumulate to a whole day. It is then taken up once in four years as leap-day. This proposal has already been fully explained.

The question now is, why do certain religious leaders make such a vigorous protest against the proposed year-end eight-day week (extending the seven-day week by one day in order to make every year begin on the same day of the week) whereas no protest whatever is made against the occurrence of numerous eight-day and six-day weeks required to cross the date line—which is the line where all days and dates end and begin—just as New Year's Day marks the point in the earth's annual journey where the years end and begin?

As a question of simple reason and common-sense, what is the difference, in so far as a violation of Divine law is involved, between the eight-day week when crossing the date line where the days and dates end and begin and the eight-day week needed to round out the calendar year when the earth passes the point in its orbit where the calendar years end and begin?

Is it real religion? Is it consistent to accept the one and oppose the other?

One is strongly tempted to believe that if the practice of using year-day and leap-day could have been so unobtrusively introduced, as was the practice of adding and dropping days at the International Date Line, both would have been equally accepted and practised as a matter of course, without protest.

CHAPTER IV

The Rivals: New York v. Honolulu

WAY BACK IN 1887 a Russian scholar with an international mind devized a plan for an international language which for a time bid fair to sweep the world and provide the solution—and a wonderfully simple solution at that—of one of the world's greatest problems: the problem of language as a barrier between the nations. He invented Esperanto.

This international language had everything, it seemed, to recommend it to the world's attention. It was, for a 'foreign' language, extremely simple and regular and easy to learn; it was demonstrated a thousand times that a smattering of it could be picked up by anyone in a matter of hours and that facility in its use for practical communication could be acquired in a very short while; that, in fact, it opened a door in an otherwise impassable brick wall which separates the nations.

Dr. Zamenoff's idea made tremendous progress, until someone else invented a 'better' international language, called 'Ido'. And then there were two. Now, although either might be universally adopted as an auxiliary tongue, which it could easily be, neither is in fact being so adopted, except by a few enthusiastic supporters of one or the other. The two systems are rivals, and the proponents of each claim their system to be the best.

But their rivalry has practically nullified the finest idea so far propounded for breaking down the world's language barricades.

A danger of the same sort is not altogether absent from the good intentions of calendar reformers. The

World Calendar plan has a rival which, being equally
well-meaning in its purpose, and very close in its main
features, is yet so different in detail as to confuse the
issue and create controversy which could lead to the
same situation as has defeated the Zamenoff ideal.

The rival idea is known as the 'Edwards Perpetual'
Calendar, and is also a twelve-month, equal-quarters
scheme. It has not achieved the international standing
of the World Calendar, but it has its own merits and it
has not hidden its light under a bushel. It is the work
of a Lieut.-Commander in the U.S. Navy, Willard E.
Edwards, whose home is at Honolulu. It reached its
apogee of importance when it got itself brought before
Congress in the United States. This has, in fact, occurred
twice. In 1944 it formed the subject of a resolution
which was passed to the Congressional Committee on
Foreign Affairs, but no further action developed. However, on March 25, 1951, the Hon. Joseph R. Farrington,
Delegate from Hawaii, rose in his seat and addressed the
House of Representatives on its behalf.

Although the speech that followed was devoted mainly
to an eulogy of the Edwards Calendar, it was also a
concise and able plea for calendar reform as such. It
revealed also the similarities of the Edwards plan to, as
well as its differences from, the World Calendar.

'The Perpetual Calendar of twelve months and equal
quarters', Farrington went on, 'is regarded by Mr.
Edwards as the logical successor to the thirteen-month
calendar proposed twenty years ago by George Eastman
of the Eastman Kodak Co. At that time Mr. Eastman
was actively engaged in furthering the adoption of a
thirteen-month calendar to replace our present irrational
one. He regarded this movement as a natural evolution
in modern life and succeeded in getting more than 100
corporations to adopt the thirteen-period calendar for
their internal accounting purposes'.

Then the speaker neatly summarized the case against the thirteen-month plan:

But auditing, inventories, production, dividends, taxes, etc., are largely and increasingly being accounted for on a quarterly basis, and most of these concerns have now returned to the customary calendar system. Thirteen cannot be split into quarters, and a double system of book-keeping proved too costly and inconvenient in most cases.

Moreover, to the average individual, thirteen identical months of four weeks each is exceedingly monotonous, and the fact that there are thirteen Fridays-the-13th in the thirteen-month calendar is very unattractive from a popular viewpoint. Also, with the 1st and 15th always on Sundays, this would cause many monthly and semi-monthly payments to be postponed or advanced and would often cause needless expense, confusion, and embarrassment.

So far, he is on familiar ground, but at this point the Edwards scheme diverges from the World Calendar. 'To begin with', Farrington went on, 'New Year's Day, an internationally celebrated holiday, is proposed not as a January 1 but as a "day apart" '. And to strengthen the general argument for the day apart he added the again familiar, but always telling, explanation: 'This is like the "extra day" we now have on crossing the date line from west to east, where two succeeding days of the week occur with the same name. This system has been successfully employed at the 180th meridian, for our convenience in reckoning days, ever since 1884 without any apparent hardship occurring to anyone.

Mr. Farrington then went on to state what is an important feature of the Edwards method. It was that 'the second day of the new year, a Monday in the Perpetual Calendar, thus becomes January 1 and will always be the first business or working day of the new year'.

He then put forward three arguments to back this point: that 'it is a real and natural need of human nature to rest after a period of work'; that 'the seventh day was the Biblical day of rest'; and that 'in actual business practice the week is already considered as beginning on Monday.' However, he added, 'for those who prefer it that way, *the Perpetual Calendar may be readily printed with Sunday as the first day*'.

The other important technical difference between the Edwards and the World calendars was then brought out.

'In this up-to-date calendar, the month lengths fall into the easily remembered pattern of 30-30-31, and the starting days into the well-known sequence of Monday-Wednesday-Friday, days on which many weekly events regularly occur. The day of the week for any day in the year can be easily figured in a few seconds by remembering '30-30-31; Monday-Wednesday-Friday'. No other rhyme or 'jingle' is necessary to compute any future date.

The first and the fifteenth, important monthly and semi-monthly, payroll, bill-paying and accounting days, always fall on week-days in the Perpetual Calendar. This plan thus becomes the most practical one for a new, fixed, up-to-date, international civil calendar.

Finally, Mr. Farrington made an eloquent and indeed a poignant appeal to Congress:

The Perpetual Calendar is offered to the United Nations for international adoption as the simplest and the most practical of any twelve-months fixed calendar yet proposed. It is an up-to-date civil calendar, entirely suitable for everyday business, social, judicial, governmental and school use. It has the main advantage of other proposals, but not their inherent disadvantages.

If Congress and the United Nations will definitely recommend that the Perpetual Calendar be universally adopted beginning with 1956, there should be plenty of time between now and then to prepare the American Ephemeris and other advance publications.

Reprinting the Perpetual Calendar itself creates reader interest and provides a clearer understanding of it. People always like to look at it to see on what day of the week their birthdays and other anniversaries will always fall. It is freely offered for the use of all nations and races, and no permission is necessary in order to reproduce it. Under unanimous consent, I ask that the Perpetual Calendar be reproduced in the Record.

A tabulated year's calendar, from Monday January 1 to Saturday December 31 is therefore set out in the Congressional Record following the report of this instructive talk. Under the same date—March 21 1951—and numbered '82nd Congress 1st Session H.R. 3397' a short Bill was introduced in the House of Representatives. Described as 'A Bill to make the calendar fixed and perpetual,' it proposed to enact that 'on and after New Year's Day 1956, the Edwards Perpetual Calendar hereinafter set out in words and figures shall be the official calendar of the United States of America and all the territories subject to its jurisdiction'. Its third clause submitted that 'the President is authorized and requested to urge upon the governments of the nations of the world at appropriate conferences that may be held and/or sessions of the United Nations and/or other international bodies, that the Edwards Perpetual Calendar be adopted, effective New Year's Day, 1956'. Again the Calendar was printed as a final clause and footnote to the Bill. (See page 214.)

Modern calendars are no less interesting, if more rational, than those of history, and before debating the merits of the Edwards plan it is illuminating to consider its origin, since that has been disputed. Commander Edwards has himself told his story in a pamphlet which he will send to anyone interested enough to ask for it.[1] In this he tells of his early interest in the subject, and how he came to work out for himself the idea of an improved calendar. From the circumstances related it

[1] Willard E. Edwards, P.O. Box 3140, Honolulu 2, Hawaii, U.S.A.

cannot be doubted that this particular design was his own. The dispute which arose later therefore as to its having been copied by him from one of the 185 proposals considered by the League of Nations Committee can only be decided in favour of the lieutenant-commander. It was 1927 before the League printed its summary of the proposals, while according to Edwards, his own idea had seen the light of print in 1922, although it did not appear again until it was given in an aircraft magazine in 1940, whence it was picked up by other journals and began to take a place among reform proposals.

THE EDWARDS PERPETUAL CALENDAR

[1]NEW YEAR'S DAY (a day apart from any week or month) is the first day of each year, a holiday, followed by the 364-day fixed calendar shown below:

January								*February*								*March*					
M	T	W	T	F	S	S		M	T	W	T	F	S	S		M	T	W	T	F	S	S
1	2	3	4	5	6	7					1	2	3	4	5					1	2	3
8	9	10	11	12	13	14		6	7	8	9	10	11	12		4	5	6	7	8	9	10
15	16	17	18	19	20	21		13	14	15	16	17	18	19		11	12	13	14	15	16	17
22	23	24	25	26	27	28		20	21	22	23	24	25	26		18	19	20	21	22	23	24
29	30							27	28	29	30					25	26	27	28	29	30	31

April								*May*								*June*					
M	T	W	T	F	S	S		M	T	W	T	F	S	S		M	T	W	T	F	S	S
1	2	3	4	5	6	7					1	2	3	4	5					1	2	3
8	9	10	11	12	13	14		6	7	8	9	10	11	12		4	5	6	7	8	9	10
15	16	17	18	19	20	21		13	14	15	16	17	18	19		11	12	13	14	15	16	17
22	23	24	25	26	27	28		20	21	22	23	24	25	26		18	19	20	21	22	23	24
29	30							27	28	29	30					25	26	27	28	29	30	31

[1]LEAP-YEAR DAY (a second day apart) is observed only in leap years between June 31 and July 1 as the first day of the second half-year, a holiday.

July								*August*								*September*					
M	T	W	T	F	S	S		M	T	W	T	F	S	S		M	T	W	T	F	S	S
1	2	3	4	5	6	7					1	2	3	4	5					1	2	3
8	9	10	11	12	13	14		6	7	8	9	10	11	12		4	5	6	7	8	9	10
15	16	17	18	19	20	21		3	16	15	16	17	18	19		11	12	13	14	15	16	17
22	23	24	25	26	27	28		20	21	22	23	24	25	26		18	19	20	21	22	23	24
29	30							27	28	29	30					25	26	27	28	29	30	31

October								*November*								*December*					
M	T	W	T	F	S	S		M	T	W	T	F	S	S		M	T	W	T	F	S	S
1	2	3	4	5	6	7					1	2	3	4	5					1	2	3
8	9	10	11	12	13	14		6	7	8	9	10	11	12		4	5	6	7	8	9	10
15	16	17	18	19	20	21		13	14	15	16	17	18	19		11	12	13	14	15	16	17
22	23	24	25	26	27	28		20	21	22	23	24	25	26		18	19	20	21	22	23	24
29	30							27	28	29	30					25	26	27	28	29	30	31

[1]These two YEAR-DAYS are definitely named and have a definite purpose. When considered apart from any week, they allow the calendar to become fixed and perpetual.

It became a rival of the World Calendar.

Therein lies the danger to both, and to the early adoption of calendar reform. It is not improbable that this rivalry is the unadmitted background of the apparent inertia of governments—most likely of the United States Government—on the subject. Twice, since the creation of the United Nations Organization this subject has been on the brink of coming up for major discussion; twice it has been postponed. The World Calendar campaign, up to the end of 1952, had got so far, but no farther, and the U.S. Government held its hand.

Yet one would imagine that from the United States would come the strongest recommendation for revision. What country more urgently needs it? What country could benefit more from the saving which must immediately result in costing and accountancy—and the time spent in these operations? The answer is surely, None. As Congressman Farrington put it to Congress: 'We make progress through adopting better methods,' and where could that be more true than in America, with its vast industries and complex business organizations? And who can doubt that American business as much or more than that of any other nation would welcome an end of the unnecessary irregularities and anomalies of the Gregorian calendar?

It is not surprising that the strongest movements for reform should have their centres in the United States. That can be said of all the major proposals: the Cotsworth (or Eastman) thirteen-month plan, as of both the World and the Edwards twelve-month devices. And as the thirteen-month idea has now been ruled out of practical politics, the politicians (on whom after all ultimate international action depends) are still left with two alternative twelve-month practical plans. Perhaps therein lies the answer. It may be that the American proponents of reform in its general sense with whom rests the deciding voice on policy find themselves in the dilemma of the philandering highwayman in *The Beggar's Opera*:

> How happy could I be with either,
> Were t'other fair charmer away?

It is most unfortunate.

It is important to look at them both, without prejudice for or against either, for it seems certain that both have to be considered. Although the World Calendar plan is best known, and has been the subject of campaigning for ten years longer than has its rival, the latter cannot be ignored or pooh-poohed. At least it has achieved the dignity of being put forward twice for a national Parliamentary approval, however much or little that may mean. (That may in fact be very little in practical effect, for private Bills of this nature are an every day occurrence, and few of them became more than a mere printed record. The World Calendar has enjoyed the same privilege several times.) On the other hand, it has no formal organization behind it, such as that of the World Calendar Association, with its headquarters office in New York and its more than thirty affiliated organizations in other countries. Nor, of course, has it risen to the distinction of having a periodical printed and circulated regularly to keep its supporters in touch with calendar history and progress such as the W.C.A.'s *Journal of Calendar Reform*. However, the Edwards calendar has received wide approbation, and has been printed in some leading journals in America, such as *New York Times*, *Christian Science Monitor* and *Collier's*. It claims eminent supporters in a number of fields.

It was the *Journal of Calendar Reform* which opened the controversy in 1944 in an article identifying the Edwards calendar with one which had been among those submitted to and eliminated by the League of Nations.

It was written by Mrs. Essy Key-Rasmussen, who had been a member of the Secretariat of the Communications and Transit Section of the League in charge of calendar reform. The article was headed boldly, PLANS ELIMINATED BY LEAGUE OF NATIONS INCLUDE DUPLICATE OF EDWARDS CALENDAR, and began: 'In the previous issue of the *Journal of Calendar Reform* considerable notice was given the Edwards Perpetual Calendar because of Resolution 39 which has been referred to the United States Congressional Committee on Foreign Affairs'.

Mrs. Key-Rasmussen went on to 'call the attention of readers of the *Journal* and the World Calendar Association itself to the fact that the Edwards Perpetual Calendar is a direct replica of Professor L. A. Grosclaude's plan which was published in Switzerland, March 1900', and generously added, lest it should be thought she was accusing the Lieutenant-Commander of deliberate plagiarism: 'It is probable that, because of the many years which have elapsed since then, Lieutenant Willard E. Edward, U.S.N.R., was unaware of this fact'.

Describing briefly the Grosclaude plan, Mrs. Key-Rasmussen wrote: 'As just mentioned, the eminent Swiss educator proposed, as early as March 1900, a perpetual twelve-month calendar of equal quarters having three months of 30, 30, 31 days and beginning the year with a Monday. It contained the annual 'blank day' to be inserted between December 31 and January 1, and Leap-Day to be inserted between June 31 and July 1. This plan was rejected by the official Swiss Committee on Calendar Reform for one based on twelve months of equal quarters, including the extra days, each quarter having three months of 31, 30, 30 days, and the year beginning with a Sunday. The latter plan, now known as the World Calendar, received the official recognition of the Federal Council of the Swiss Government on June 1 1931'. Then followed notes on other plans which had equally been 'eliminated by the Communications

P

and Transit Committee and also by the International
Conference held in Geneva in 1931'.

This was a sharp attack, although it was likely perhaps
to be inimical rather more to the claimant to authorship
of the rival calendar than to the calendar itself. Naturally
it called for a reply, and no doubt explains the pains the
lieutenant-commander has taken to print in his explanatory pamphlet the otherwise unnecessary story of its
origin. However, it was not for some six years that
Willard Edwards answered back in kind, when in
December 1950 he wrote to Mrs. Key-Rasmussen:

> I hardly need point out that after I took the trouble to
> investigate your article, I found the exact calendar which Miss
> Achelis has been publicizing all these years—and without any
> credit to the man who introduced it to the League, namely,
> Mr. Octavius Smith's plan (File 45266 on page 32 of the
> League's publication C.167.M.49.1927.VIII). Could the pot
> be calling the kettle black?
>
> I had never heard of Professor Grosclaude before, but found
> his plan on page 29 of the above publication, File 34973; after
> reading your article. He begins the year on January 1st, I on
> 'New Year's day', the day *preceding* January 1st. His annual
> day apart is the last day of the year; mine is the first day of the
> year. His leap-year day is the 183rd day of the year; mine is
> the 184th. He suggests Easter on April 7th; I on April 14th.
> And doesn't he start his weeks with Sunday: I start mine with
> Monday. Do you think you owe me an apology or not?

It was a fair enough counter-stroke, even though it
had been so long delayed, and in quoting the letter in the
Journal in which the original article had appeared, it gave
Mrs. Rasmussen the opportunity to express regret at
having overlooked 'minor differences' between the two
plans, and not only to set these side by side in tabulated
form, but also to reply to the counter-accusation directed
to the World Calendar. On this point the reply pointed
out that Miss Achelis had never claimed to have origin-

ated the World Calendar and quoted from Miss Achelis's book *The Calendar for Everybody* published 1943:

> The World Calendar gradually evolved from Switzerland as a result of a study made at the request of the International Congress of Chambers of Commerce in 1914 and later through the activities of the League of Nations. Many minds have contributed, valuable historical facts have been unearthed, greater knowledge and understanding have been gained, and yet no one can claim it—the World Calendar.

The three systems made an interesting comparison, set out in the style in which the League had published in 1927 all the different proposals submitted up to that time. They looked like this:

EDWARDS PLAN

Proposer's Name: Willard E. Edwards

Date of Proposal: Newspaper Clippings 1941

Summary of Basis

1. Twelve months of 30, 30, 31 days.
2–3. Year to begin with 'New Year's Day', the annual blank day, which is followed by Monday, 1 January.
4. Leap Day to be inserted between 31 June and 1 July, as the first day of the second half-year.

GROSCLAUDE PLAN

Proposer's Name: L. A. Grosclaude

Date of Proposal: March 1900

League of Nations File No. 34973.

Summary of Basis

1. Twelve months of 30, 30, 31 days.
2. Year to begin on Monday, 1 January.
3. The annual blank day to be inserted between 31 December and 1 January.
4. Leap day to be inserted between 31 June and 1 July.
5. Easter to be on 7 April, fixed.

SMITH PLAN

Proposer's Name: Octavius Smith
Date of Proposal: 18 May, 1925
League of Nations File No. 45266

Summary of Basis

1. Twelve months of 31, 30, 30 days.
2. The year to begin on Sunday, 1 January.
3. The annual blank day to be on 31 December (New Year's Eve).
4. Leap-day to be on 31 June (Peace Day).
5. Easter to be on 8 April, fixed.

Now the essential thing which this curious controversy brings out is that all these calendar ideas (and a good many more of the League's 185) have the key to really desirable reform. They dispose of that bane of all calendar-makers, the awkward and irreconcilable 365th day of the year, and its quadrennial twin nuisance the 366th by treating them as intercalary 'days apart'. The basic principle is the same throughout, and has been the fundamental of every sound proposition since it was first advanced by Hirassa ap-Iccim in his classic letter to the *Gentleman's Magazine* in 1745: whether the general design implied dividing the remaining 364 days into thirteen months or into twelve. Moreover, once the principle is applied, any calendar is a perpetual calendar, for only its ease of reference and workaday convenience are dependent on its internal shape. One is tempted to wonder that the idea, so simple and so beneficent, did not in fact occur to that genius Julius Cæsar, who came so near to exactitude and was prepared in any case to be revolutionary. However, it did not, and we are still left to work it out for ourselves on the basis of the ancient Roman twelve months. (For the purpose of this argument, the thirteen-month plans may be regarded as rejected.)

The similarity of the Edwards and World calendars goes an important step further. Both divide the year into four equal quarters, each with 91 days. It is in the layout of these quarters—30, 30, 31 *versus* 31, 30, 30—and in the positioning of the intercalary days, the days apart, that divergence lies. Both sides claim superiority. Both have been at pains to explain why. Reduced to essentials, the differences lie in or about the facts that whereas the World Calendar begins its year and its quarters on a Sunday, the Edwards plan makes the first day of the year and the quarter a Monday; and that consequently whereas in the World Calendar the year-end day, the stabilizing day falls between Saturday and Sunday, that in the Edwards version is placed after the Sunday and before the Monday. A result of this, of which its author makes much, is that the World idea would tend to create a four-day weekend holiday, at the New Year, which he argues would not be acceptable to business men and would bring New Year's Eve into a position which churchmen would not like—an argument which seems somewhat strained.

On the other side, the New York reaction to the Honolulu claims followed the first submission of the Edwards plan to Congress by Mr. Farrington on September 27 1943. After pointing out that 'The World Calendar Association, Inc., being educational in its activities,' was precluded from 'fostering legislation'[1] the Journal of Calendar Reform (third quarter, 1944)

---

[1] A World Calendar Bill was in fact similarly introduced in both the U.S. House of Representatives and the Senate in 1946. It had support from both political parties, and particulars will be found in the *Journal of Calendar Reform*, 1946, and in the *Congressional Record* of July 15 1946, pages 7174, 9175; and A 4380 and A 4381; July 16 1946, page 9284; August 1 1946, pages 10765, 10766 and 10767. Similar Bills were introduced in both Houses in 1947, and in the Senate by the distinguished Senator Estes Kefauver in 1948.

set out the following 'contrasting differences' in the two calendars:

EDWARDS CALENDAR	WORLD CALENDAR
Begins the year with a dateless day and every quarter on a Monday, the second day of the week.	Begins the year and every quarter on a *Sunday*, the *first* day of the week. Monday January 2 begins the business year because Sunday, New Year's day, is preceded by a World holiday.
Allocates the days in the three months of every quarter as 30, 30, 31, thereby giving every month 26 week-days, plus Sundays.	Allocates the days in the three months of each quarter as 31, 30, 30, which gives to every month 26 weekdays, plus Sundays.
Begins the civil year and the week with the proverbial 'blue Monday'—a slow pick up.	Begins the civil year and the week with the customary Sunday —an uplift.
To begin the year and the week on a business day, Monday, a materialistic beginning, will rob people of higher and nobler motives with which to start every year and every week.	To begin the year and the week with a spiritual Sunday will continue to inspire people with higher motives with which to start every year and week.
Places Monday as the first day of the week, which, in turn, makes the Hebrew Sabbath the sixth day instead of the seventh day, and the Christian Sunday the seventh day instead of the first day of the week.	Keeps Sunday as the first day of the week that commemorates the Resurrection, and the Sabbath remains the seventh day of the week that recognizes the Hebrew day of rest.
The arbitrary rearrangement of the days within the week will increase opposition among the Churches. The change is unnecessarily drastic.	By retaining the arrangement of the week, has received numerous endorsements from the Churches.

Ends every quarter with a Sunday, a day of worship. This will cause difficulty and confusion for general bookkeeping. Statisticians, accountants and all those who wish to close their books at the end of every quarter will either have to advance the day to Saturday or postpone it to Monday, the beginning of a new quarter.

Avoids these difficulties, since every quarter ends with a Saturday, the last day of the business week, and does not interfere with the day of worship, Sunday.

'Incidentally', avoids Friday-the-13ths thus appeasing the superstitious.

Reduces Friday-the-13ths to only four (in the first month of every quarter) considering superstition as negligible.

According to the press, has the approval of the Honolulu Junior Chamber of Commerce and dozens of large companies. It has also been favourably received by Massachusetts Institute of Technology, Oklahoma and Southern California Universities.

Has the official approval of 14 nations. Among the influential groups of American Association for the Advancement of Science, Committee for Maritime Meteorology, Commission 32 of the International Astronomical Union; Mathematical Association of America, American Industrial Bankers' Association, American Institute of Accountants; the London, British and Empire Chambers of Commerce, and the Chicago Association of Commerce; National and World Education Associations, the General Federation of Women's Clubs and the National Federation of Business and Professional Women's Clubs have all approved it. Other endorsements have been published.

So far as it has gone, the rivalry has not done much harm, at least in Britain. Both have had a certain amount of newspaper publicity, and in that way each has done its part in attracting attention to the outstanding need for modernization of the calendar. Probably not many who have had their calendar-consciousness stirred have taken a deep enough interest in the matter to go into detail. Few probably have realized that there are alternative possibilities. But as the campaign develops and interest in the subject quickens—as it is very much to be hoped it will do in the next year or two—it is not going to help the cause if there is confusion as to what the new calendar is going to be, and if support is to be divided between rival claims.

In America, one cannot help but feel, much harm has already been done. Although in official circles this rivalry has never been mentioned, it is inevitably in the background. 'How much longer will the world tolerate its absurd, unreasonable calendar, one that not only hinders the efficiency of business and industry but also brings inconvenience and disorder to all our administrative, social and domestic activities?' asked the *Journal of Calendar Reform* in 1951, and continued:

The question applies with special force to leaders of public opinion *in the United States*, because there seems to be greater apathy and indifference to calendar reform there than in other lands. Canada to the north has repeatedly expressed its approval of the World Calendar, and so has Mexico on the opposite frontier. Central and South Americans too have demonstrated a keen desire for calendar change. During recent years, seventeen governments have approved the World Calendar in principle; *but the United States has been the laggard*. This government, in every instance, has lamentably displayed a do-nothing policy. In the laudable endeavour of the United Nations to move toward a better calendar, it has been the United States delegation which has stood in the way of progress.

Two years ago the World Calendar was on the preliminary agenda of the General Assembly, when the United States delegation insisted on postponement, urging that the agenda was too crowded and in a previous instance that other subjects were 'more urgently important'.

Obviously, the world must choose. Just as general opinion has discarded, in the case of the earlier choice, the thirteen-month reformed calendar, with all its attractions, in favour of the more practical twelve-month plan, so again it must decide between the two twelve-month alternatives; the Sunday-starting week or the Monday-starting. It is that point which is at issue: shall the week begin on a Sunday, as in the World Calendar, or shall it start on a Monday as in the Edwards design?

The arguments on the whole are very much in favour of Sunday. It is the natural and established day, and from that point of view would mean less dislocation— an all-important point, in this writer's opinion. While conceding that Edward's idea of the Monday start is perhaps more logical in a strictly business world, it is only in that business sense that it has any superior claim—and the world is not all strictly business. There must be some compromise with the traditional, not to say the aesthetic. The other points Edwards makes, all arising out of this basic difference, are not important— the question of the long year-end week-end, for example. That will fit itself into either scheme.

Beyond this comparison of the merits of the rival calendars there is the matter of the progress already made. Here the comparison is all in favour of the World Calendar. The World Calendar Association is in existence, has done a tremendous amount of proselytizing work, has done much research, and has spent an incalculable amount of money in bringing calendar reform to notice and overcoming general inertia with regard to it. It has organized and is actively prosecuting a definite campaign. It has spread the gospel of calendar reform over a large part of the world. Its calendar, moreover, has no disadvantages which anything in the Edwards calendar can overcome without creating other and equal disadvantages.

It is obvious that the final decision must rest with the United Nations, but because there will always be some ground for advancing the plea of 'more urgently important' matters, the less controversy there is on this subject the better. Is it then too much to hope that Lieutenant-Commander Willard Edwards will drop his alternative plan and, since he desires reform as ardently as any, lend his authority and weight to the support of the World Calendar? This is a plea put forward to him with great respect and no lack of admiration for his brilliant plan, to do so.

It is addressed also to the other authors of calendar proposals whom Mr. Trygve Lie had in mind when he stated in his Report on Calendar Reform in 1947:

> Nine other proposals for calendars were included in correspondence received. Despite a great variety of type, they nearly all had some similarity with the numerous drafts considered by the League of Nations. The year consisting of thirteen months of 28 days each was again submitted by many people. A year in equal quarters each composed of months of 28, 28 and 35 days successively and a year of 73 five-day weeks also appeared. . . .

There is also the decimal calendar project being actively advocated by Mr. George W. Szwede, of Los Angeles,[1] to whom the same appeal is made, as it is to Mr. E. K. Eason, of Dublin,[2] who advocates a scheme for utilizing Christmas Day as the extra-calendrical day in the last week of the year.

---

[1] Author: George W. Szwede, 8518 Sunset Boulevard, Los Angeles 46, California, U.S.A.

[2] Author: E. K. Eason, 40–41 Lower O'Connell Street, Dublin.

CHAPTER V

Chaos in India

NO COMMENTATOR ON this side of the world is required to point the moral with regard to the calendar situation in India. The most illuminating possible comment was made by Dr. K. D. Malaviya, Indian Deputy Minister for Natural Resources, when he said early in 1953: 'India is today using more than thirty different calendars, a situation which is chaotic and intolerable'.

The occasion on which this revealing statement was made was the opening of a sitting of a committee at Delhi to study the calendar question. This committee has been officially appointed to make recommendations to the Government of India as to how the problem can best be dealt with. Certain extremely interesting recommendations have in fact already been made. In no country is action more urgently needed. Because of this, and because the first steps to such action have been taken in making this official study of the question, it is possible that India may play a vital part in bringing about a desirable reform not only for herself but, by showing and leading the way, for other countries also.

It is perhaps an indication of the complexity of the Indian situation that various authorities and commentators on Indian calendars rarely agree as to the number in vogue. Whereas an authority like the Deputy Minister quoted above mentions 'more than thirty', an equally eminent authority in the person of Professor M. N. Saha, F.R.S., President of the Astronomical and Astrophysical Society of India and an Indian M.P., wrote recently: 'In India there have been twenty-five

227

different kinds of calendars in use',[1] while in 1944 Carleton J. Ketchum, a distinguished international journalist, reported: 'India today employs fourteen principal or important calendars in addition to the Gregorian, Mohammedan and Jewish'.[2]

Professor Saha divides his list into three categories:

(1) Calendars of purely Indian origin;

(2) Calendars of foreign origin: Christian, Hijira, Tarikh-Ilahi;

(3) Hybrid calendars, which came into existence in the wake of Akber's introduction of Tarikh-Ilahi;

but points out that some of the purely Indian calendars are now extinct, although knowledge of them is necessary for the historian. He quotes the late S. B. Dixit, Indian pioneer authority on the study of calendars, as distinguishing three periods in the country's calendar development:

(1) The Vedic period from an unknown period antiquity to 1350 B.C.;

(2) The Vedanga Jyotish period from 1350 B.C. to A.D. 400.

(3) The Siddhanta Jyotish period from A.D. 400 to modern times.

For historical purposes the Indian problem is largely one of eras, or rather systems of astronomy, or siddhantas, used in different eras in the country's history, while the current problem is related more nearly to geography. Ketchum enumerates the following calendar systems in use in different regions:

Assamese	used in Assam
Bengali	„ Bengal Province
Burmese	„ Burma and parts of Bengal
Gujrati	„ Bombay province
Hindu	„ All parts of India

[1] 'The Reform of the Indian Calendar' by M. N. Saha in *Science and Culture* (Calcutta), August 1952.

[2] Journal of Calendar Reform, Vol. 14.

CHAOS IN INDIA 229

Kanarese	,,	Mysore, West India and parts of Madras
Mahashtra	,,	South of Bombay, Poona and elsewhere
Malayi	,,	Malabar
Marwari	,,	Marwar States and by merchants throughout India
Oriya	,,	Orissa, part of Madras and greater part of Behar
Parsi	,,	Many parts of India
Punjabi (Bikremi)	,,	Punjab Province
Yamil	,,	South of India (and Ceylon)
Telegu	,,	North of Madras

and describes his own experience:

Travelling in India as I was privileged to do in 1930 when my interviews with public personalities ranged all the way from Mohandas Gandhi to Viscount Halifax, then Britain's Viceroy at New Delhi, I discerned this extraordinary calendar tangle. It was apparent in the native newspapers and in other directions throughout the country. Indian Government officials stressed it as a source of embarrassment and cost to the Indian exchequer. The extent of this embarrassment and cost may be gauged when I explain that the Government has long printed four of these calendars—the Bengali, Hindu, Malayi and Tamil—in the form of an almanac which includes the Gregorian and Mohammedan styles. This almanac has usually consisted of about 3,000 pages and is required to cover the meridian transits of the sun, moon and important stars for each day in a succession of years. The work of compilation, it was explained to me, requires at least three months and often much more. The aim of the almanac is to determine and publicise for the edification of all concerned the seasons, festivals and holidays and co-ordinate all historical dates.

The *Surya Siddhanta*, the best known system of Indian astronomy, is believed to have been current in its present form since the eleventh century A.D., and is the official standard for all India. Several other siddhantas are extant, but only one of them, the *Arya*

Siddhanta, is of any practical importance in southern India.[1] Indian time is kept in *ghatkas*, or sixtieth parts of a day, each *ghatka* being equivalent to 24 minutes of English time, or two-fifths of an hour; and in *palas*, a *pala* being a sixtieth part of a *ghatka*. The *ghatkas* and *palas* are reckoned, not from midnight to midnight as in English time, but from sunrise to sunrise. In the same way, the Indian *tithi*, which is almost but not quite the equivalent of the English day, is the thirtieth part of the lunar month (of 29·530588) days.

These time units are peculiar to India, and render the comparison of Indian and European times particularly difficult. However, for official reasons, the civil day of twenty-four hours is also employed, and adequate almanacs, such as the scholarly *Indian Ephemeris* are available for easy conversion. The civil day (with its multiple, the week) is the one measure of time which is common to European and Indian reckoning, everything else (year, month, ghatkas, palas, hours, minutes, seconds) being different in the two systems.

The fact that the Indian day, or *tithi*, begins strictly at the moment of sunrise, is perhaps the most difficult factor in comparison, and, states the *Ephemeris*, 'as the moment of sunrise depends on the latitude and longitude of each place, there should, strictly speaking, be as many *panchangas* (or calendars) as there are places in India. Indian astronomers got over this difficulty by calculating time in the first instance according to one central latitude and longitude and then applying the necessary corrections in order to deduce the time at other places. The central latitude is the equator and the central longitude is that of Ujjain (75″ 46′ 6° east of Greenwich), where there was an ancient observatory. To combine the central latitude and the central longitude, they imagined an island called *Lanka* in the Indian Ocean, situated on the equator and having the same longitude as Ujjain.'

[1] *An Indian Ephemeris* (Govt. Press, Madras).

(This reference to Ujjain in the standard current work on Indian time-reckoning is interesting, for it is in the region of the same point that it is now proposed to centre a new national system, as we shall see).

The *tithi* in the Hindu calendar is a unique conception, indigenous to India, and while it is counted from sunrise to sunrise, it has in the past and in some parts of India operated from moonset to moonset or from moonrise to moonrise. It is defined as the time-period when the moon gains 12° on the sun, beginning from the *moment* when conjunction of the moon with the sun is completed. But while the tithi is essentially a factor of the moon and the lunar month it is linked also to the solar year. The month is divided into two halves—the *shudh* or *shukla paksh* (the clean or bright half) and the *vadhya* or *krishna paksh* (the dark half). Each half-month has fifteen tithis, which average 23 hours 37 minutes. They are numbered, but by *sanskit* and not by vernacular numbers, e.g., the first is called *Pratipada*, the second *Dwitya*, and the third *Tritya*, the fourth *Chaturthi*, and so on to the fifteenth *Pornima*, or full-moon day. The second half is numbered in the same way but the fifteenth is not called Pornima; it is called Amawasha, or 'living together'. It is believed that because there is no moon visible and the sun and moon are in the same quarter, they are living together.[1]

Throughout the Bombay Presidency the months have similar names, but south of the Narbada River, the first month is Chaitra (March and April). North of the Narbada the Hindu years begin on the first of Kartik (October and December). In the same way two different eras apply historically; north of the Narbada, the *Samwat* era which began in 56 B.C., and south of that river the *Shaliwaham* era, dating from A.D. 78.

In the same way there are two Mohammedan year

[1] C. A. Kincaid, 'The Romance of the Indian Calendar', *Journal of the Royal Asiatic Society*, Parts 3 and 4, 1943.

systems (or at any rate were before the separation of
Pakistan and India in 1947), but, says C. A. Kincaid, the
Parsi calendar is perhaps the most romantic of all. It is
the same as the old Persian calendar. It was the practice
of every Sassanide king of Persia to found a new era
when he ascended the throne; but he always closed the
first year of his era on the 21st March. Since Yazdagird,
the last Sassanide king of Persia—and the Parsis have
never recognized any of his successors as *de jure* rulers—
began his reign on June 16, A.D. 632, the present year
of the Parsi era should be 1311. It is actually 1312.
The difference is due to the absence of any intercalation
since Yadagird's death.

In connection with this the same author relates an
interesting incident in Indian calendar history.

The Parsis have no weekdays but they have twelve
months each of 30 days, both months and days having
separate names. To the total of 360 days, five more days,
known as *gathas*, are added. These are named after the
gathas or holy hymns of Zoroaster. To adjust the 365
days to the seasons the ancient Persians intercalated a
month of 30 days (*kabisa*) every 120 years; but after the
downfall of the Sassanide kingdom the fugitive Zoroastrians (i.e. the Parsis) omitted the intercalation. The
Zoroastrians who remained in Persia remembered to do
so, but once only. When some centuries later both sections met in India, it was found that the Parsis began
their new year a month later than the other section, now
known as Iranis, that is to say, the Parsis began their
year in September, and the Iranis in August. This led to
a bitter controversy, only allayed when it was found that
both sections were wrong. Had the old Persian system of
intercalation been correctly maintained, the new year
would have begun neither in August nor in September
but on March 21, the day of the vernal equinox.

Such illustrations serve to indicate the confused calendrical situation in the sub-continent, but at the same

time it has to be admitted that India has carried on under these difficulties, not unsuccessfully, for a very long time. No doubt it is being said, in India as elsewhere, that the people have got along very well under existing conditions. Perhaps, so far as business and administration are concerned, they have, but with regard to the ordinary people the following quotation from Professor Saha's pamphlet[1] is all the commentary required:

Today in India, for the determination of the 'propitious' date and moment for all sorts of activities and observances, the people are entirely dependent on astrologers, who pretend to possess the knowledge to produce such information from the ancient formulas. In order to compel obedience and a uniformity of practice, the astrologers have invented 'divine punishment' for people who dare to carry out life's ordinary activities without consulting them or without observing their requirements.

Our people have become hopelessly dependent on the astrologer and subject to the hallucinations he has invented, which have deprived them of freedom of judgment and enterprise. A thoughtful person might well ask regarding these divine punishments, 'Has God Almighty the mentality of a village pedagogue that he will inflict a severe punishment on a sincere devotee for committing an arithmetical mistake?'

The dates and moments of auspicious days are given by different combinations of ancient astrological elements, for which it is not possible to find any scientific justification. Moreover, as the ancient calculations do not agree with the actual positions of the heavenly bodies, what importance can be attached to these astrological sanctions? The accumulated error is now nearly twenty-three days, and the astrologer's calculations have long since reached the stage of total absurdity.

The 23 days error to which the Professor refers is the result of the neglect by early Indian astronomers of the precession of the equinoxes, and although the phenom-

[1] Professor M. N. Saha, F.R.S., *Calendar Reform in India* (World Calendar Association).

enon has now long been recognized, Indian astronomy continues to suffer from the limitations imposed by its early history. From this point of view added importance is attached to the present movement for the creation of a unified calendar system, and a revival of astronomical study. The movement took shape in 1952 when Mr. Nehru, as Prime Minister, appointed a Calendar Reform Committee of the Council of Scientific and Industrial Research to study the whole complicated subject and make recommendations. Included on this committee were the Minister of Education, Dr. Maulana Kalam Azad, Professor Saha, and a number of distinguished Indian scientists. Its consultants included the Director of the Indian Standards Institution, Dr. Lal C. Verman; the Joint Director of Archæology, A. Ghosh; K. G. Krishnamurti, of the Council of Scientific and Industrial Research, S. Basu of the Meteorological Service, and other leaders of scientific activity in the country.

The first full-sessional meeting of the new committee proved fruitful, and the recommendations resulting from it, and now (1953) before the Indian Government for consideration, may well lead to a re-vitalization of the science of astronomy in India, as well as putting an end to the country's calendar confusions for the future—the past will remain always an intriguing complexity for historians.

The Committee agreed to recommend the establishment of a new central observatory—an 'Indian Greenwich'—from which the basic astronomical and scientific data on time measurement would be distributed to the entire country. It was voted that this observatory should be located on the meridian $82\frac{1}{2}°$ east of Greenwich and in the approximate latitude of the ancient cultural centre and observatory of Ujjain.

This would bring the 'Indian Standard Meridian' half-way between the meridian of Calcutta and the meridian of Delhi. Nautical and aviation tables would be compiled, so that ships and aircraft could navigate throughout the terrain of India and neighbouring areas by calculations based on this fixed line. Time signals, issued at stated times from this central observatory, would tally with these tables. Meantime a necessary uniformity in the elements of time measurement would be established and enforced by the observatory.

It was recommended further that the new establishment should be equipped with the latest modern telescope and instruments similar to those used at Hurstmonceux Castle (the new English 'Greenwich') and at the U.S. Naval Observatory at Washington, and that complete lunar-solar calendars should be compiled for at least five years in advance, to include all information required for navigation as well as for the accurate calculation of religious festivals and other data of local importance in various districts.

The Committee's task, it was stated by Dr. Malaviya in his opening address, was two-fold: First, it must evolve and establish a scientific system acceptable in all areas and communities in India; and, secondly, it must encourage and advance the international plans for reform of the Gregorian calendar to help evolve a more scientific system for the whole world. Beyond this, the committee registered its unanimous opinion that the implementation of this unified calendar should be in the hands of, so far at least as India was concerned, 'a central astronomical observatory, equipped with modern instruments like the ammonia clock, the quartz clock, and the rest, for perfected time signal service and for geophysical studies'. It was agreed that the observatory should be located in longitude 82·5° E and latitude 23° N.

There seems to be every reason to expect that the committee's recommendations will be adopted, and the fact that it came out so strongly in favour of general reform of the calendar, outside as well as inside its own boundaries, should have its influence on world opinion.

That it is already doing so was reflected when, at a meeting of the British Section of the World Calendar Association held in London in May 1953, Mr. Peter Freeman, M.P., a member of the British committee of that Association, pointed out that those interested in the matter in this country were 'looking to India, who were in a particularly strong position to raise the question at the forthcoming meeting of the Economic and Social Council of the United Nations'.

How well this expectation was justified was proved when in October there was circulated to members of the Economic and Social Council copies of a 'communication to the Secretary-General from the Permanent Representative of India to the United Nations'.[1]

'The Government of India', the communication stated, 'consider that the plan for the reform of the Gregorian Calendar proposed by the World Association is of great importance to the nations of the world'.

It went on: 'The purpose of the plan is to adopt for the whole world, from January 1, 1956, a new, fixed, uniform and invariable calendar, regulated astronomically according to the movement of the Earth around the Sun, and more regular, scientific and advantageous than the Gregorian Calendar.

'*It is, therefore, requested that the plan for the reform of the calendar be included in the agenda for the eighteenth session of the Economic and Social Council to be held in 1954*'.

Together with this communication there was circulated a memorandum submitted by the Indian Permanent Representative which neatly summarized the case for reform (see Appendix A).

It is possible that India will prove to be the pivot on which international, and indeed universal, action for reform may turn.

[1] E/2514 30 Oct., '53.

CHAPTER VI

The English Story

ENGLISH INTEREST IN calendar reform has been fitful and spasmodic. Now and again there has been a surge of enthusiasm when a few keen and forward-looking persons got together and sought to generate some general interest and action, but these moments have mainly served to punctuate long periods of apathy when the whole thing seemed to be forgotten.

In early days English scholars had much to do with pointing out the defect of drift in the old Julian calendar and to that extent were responsible for the reform in 1582, but it was almost against the national will that the same reform was at last adopted in the United Kingdom 170 years later. When that had settled down, we seem to have carried on without giving the matter much thought until well into the twentieth century. The first time the suggestion was raised that further reform was desirable appears to have been at an International Congress of Chambers of Commerce in 1910, following which the Council of the London Chamber decided 'to urge the Foreign Office to entertain favourably the invitation which the Swiss Government were proposing to extend to Great Britain to be represented at an International Diplomatic Conference at Geneva'.

Arising out of that it is on record that 'at a later meeting the Council expressed the opinion that in addition to being represented at the Conference, the Government should give its support to the proposals to establish, by international agreement, a Fixed International Calendar and a Fixed Date for Easter'.

At this time the thirteen-month calendar plan was being advocated by Moses B. Cotsworth, and Lord Desborough, who was then president of the London Chamber of Commerce, was keenly interested in it. From that date in fact Desborough kept the subject alive in official places, and with his backing the Cotsworth scheme got a good deal of intermittent publicity. The Cotsworth organization, known as the International Fixed Calendar League, opened an office in London.

Lord Desborough's strongest interest, however, was concerned with the question of stabilizing Easter, and mention of a fixed Easter occurs continually throughout the records of resolutions and movements connected with this business of calendar reform. By 1912 a Bill to stabilize Easter had been brought into the House of Commons and there was support not only from commercial organizations such as Chambers of Commerce but also the Universities of London, Leedsand Manchester. Nothing however came of it, and World War I put an end to this activity for a while, but it was resumed again afterwards and one of the earliest radio talks on record was a broadcast on 'A Fixed Easter' by Lord Desborough.

There followed then the long, serious and valuable investigation of the whole calendar reform question by the League of Nations, during which in 1928 the English Easter Act was passed (though destined to lie on the shelf), and ultimately Easter was more or less sorted out and segregated from the general calendar question. By this time English interest in the matter had pretty well died. The English were bored.

However, Mr. Cotsworth was doing his best to keep the subject before us. His office in Lower Regent Street was busy, and from time to time issued propaganda pamphlets and supplied information to the newspapers and anyone else who asked for it. Among his League's publications were records of his own research into ancient calendar lore as well as disquisitions on current calendar defects and recommendations for reform. But interest had waned.

It revived a little in the early nineteen-thirties. There was a spurt of interest in the fourth conference of the Transit and Communications Committee of the League of Nations when the sub-committee on calendar reform met to consider the report we have discussed in earlier chapters. It was at this time that Miss Achelis, of New York, appeared at Geneva with her new World Calendar plan.

The World Calendar cause was taken up by Mr. C. David Stelling, to whom it appealed, and from about 1931 the movement for the adoption of this calendar centred about the Parliament-Street Office of Mr. Stelling.

At this time also Elisabeth Achelis herself spent some time in London making it her headquarters for visits to other European countries and to many leaders in Britain in the commercial, educational, religious and social fields. She obtained a great deal of support for her calendar.

Among the numerous influential people who saw new hope for the ultimate solution of the problem in the streamlined Achelis twelve-month, equal-quarter World Calendar, with its obvious advantages over the sharp-angled thirteen-month Cotsworth proposal were a number of M.P.'s, who decided to form their own association to promote and publicize this plan in preference to the already well-known Cotsworth one. Thus there came into being the Rational Calendar Association, with Sir Philip Richardson, M.P. for Chelsea, as its Chairman, and C.D. Stelling as secretary.

London now had two active calendar reform groups: the International Fixed Calendar League recommending the thirteen-month proposal, and the Rational Calendar Association, sponsoring the new twelve-month, equal-

quarter idea. Each put forward its own cause energetically at Geneva. Equally energetically it propagated the
superior advantages of its own version of reform at home.

However, it was at Geneva that the decision had to be
made, for obviously neither Britain nor any other nation
was likely to take any official individual action while the
general question was under consideration by the League
of Nations. In the next few years both Mr. Stelling and
Mr. Cotsworth each made several appearances at the
League of Nations headquarters, and slowly the twelve-
month plan established itself as the more practical and
desirable solution.

The situation immediately before the war we have
already discussed. It was summarized in a final circular
issued by the Rational Calendar Association in August
1939 as a Progress Report.

'The year 1937', it said, 'marked a turning point in the
history of the movement. Early in that year the League
of Nations Council (on which Great Britain's representative was Mr. Anthony Eden) unanimously endorsed a
moderate and practical plan for revision and by its action
converted an ideal into an officially acknowledged plan
of reform. This plan was the World Calendar, known in
this country as the Desborough plan or Rational Calendar, advocated by the Rational Calendar Association in
Great Britain, the World Calendar Association in the
U.S.A., and the Committee for the Reform of the
Calendar in France'.

It went on then to describe the procedure of the
League which we have noted in sending out its questionnaire to member nations, and concluded:

'Subsequently, 14 Governments accepted the scheme
and only six were opposed. But as the majority of
Governments hesitated to come to a decision, the quasi-
unanimity necessary to call an international conference
was not achieved. In consequence, the Technical and
Advisory Committee on Transit and Communications

(within whose province calendar reform lies) had no alternative but to recommend, in its report, that further consideration of the question should be postponed for the time being. At the same time it reaffirmed the opinion expressed in the Draft Convention in stating that the social and economic advantages to be derived from the reform were "incontestable" '.

That was the recorded progress in August 1939. World War II opened in the following month, and calendar reform went into cold storage. So did the Rational Calendar Association, in this case for keeps, for there were no further meetings.

Before that potent date, however, there had been one other interesting event. That was a debate on the subject in the House of Lords.

It took place on March 4 1936, when Lord Merthyr 'rose to ask His Majesty's Government whether it proposed to take any steps to accelerate, at the forthcoming meeting of the Transit Section of the League of Nations, the adoption by international action of a fixed calendar; and to move for Papers.'[1] It was chiefly remarkable for the clear enunciation of the then Archbishop of Canterbury of his approval of the calendar reform principle.

Lord Merthyr put forward the calendar case much as we have already seen it; explained how the League's investigation had proved immensely valuable in examining hundreds of proposals and reducing them to two— the alternatives of the thirteen-month, and the twelve-month equal-quarter designs. What was wanted now, he said, was 'a lead from His Majesty's Government—a lead at Geneva, and a lead, if I may respectfully say so, a little different from that which was given in the year 1931, when the Transit Section last met. At that meeting a representative of the British Government attended, and, without in any way wishing to criticize him as an individual, I would like to say that the attitude which he was

[1] *Parliamentary Debates*, House of Lords, March 4 1936.

no doubt instructed to take at that meeting did not inspire confidence in those who want this reform. . . . He said in one passage:

> The vote which had just been taken would not be any help to Governments in forming an opinion. He himself had not been able to do anything else but abstain because if he said Yes, that would have implied that he agreed that there were advantages, and if he had said No, that would have implied that there were no advantages. As far as he was concerned, neither of these indications would have been true.

'That', Lord Merthyr went on to submit, 'was not a constructive or hopeful statement, and I ask that in 1936 something more definite may go from here to Geneva. Because there is evidence here to show that the rest of the world desires and expects a lead from this country. Those members of organizations concerned who travel in the world experience this sort of statement: "If only your Government would do something about this we could get on with it." And again they say: "But the British Government would be the slowest of all to accept this reform" '.

Lord Desborough took up the case, but dealt mainly with that side of it in which he was most interested—the stabilization of Easter, and the failure of the churches to come to agreement for action—and on this he made one particularly telling point.

'With the indulgence of the House', he said, 'I should like to explain that last year a very important delegation went to Rome on behalf of the World Calendar Association of the United States. It was instituted by the Rational Calendar Association of this country. This mission was supported by letters of delegation from the United States World Calendar Association, the Latin American Committees on Calendar Reform, the Bureau d'Etudes of Paris, and the Gesellschaft of Calendar Reform of Berlin. The important thing is that it was headed by a very celebrated Roman Catholic ecclesiastic, the Right Reverend Fernand Cabrol, Abbot of St. Michael's, Farnborough. He is one of the greatest authorities in the Roman Catholic Church, has written no fewer than twelve books on the subject and is one of the editors of the *Roman Catholic Encyclopedia*. The important thing is that a Roman Catholic ecclesiastic of his eminence should come forward to support these two proposals—namely, the reform of the calendar and a fixed date for Easter. He submitted in Latin a Memorandum representing the views of all these various associations, which is now placed on record in the archives of the Vatican'.

Lord Desborough then quoted the start of the Memorandum:

> On the reform of the calendar. Throughout all Christian nations today is spread a strong desire for a reform of the Gregorian Calendar;

and after reading some extracts relating specifically to Easter, he continued: 'Then the Memorandum says:

> 'The proposal to set aside one day out of the days of the week. . . .

'this is in reference to the proposed calendar reform—

> is similarly intended for the general benefit of mankind and the promotion of Christian unity. Its purpose is to enable the remaining 364 days of the year to be divided into fifty-two whole weeks, so that every year should begin on a Sunday and all the dates of the months fall always on the same days of the week. By this means a perpetual calendar would be established for all time.
>
> 'This proposal is not necessarily of prime concern to the Church; it need only affect lay interest. But it would obviously be more acceptable to public opinion if it were accorded the sanction of the Church's authority. No Christian Community that has studied the question has found any objection to the

proposal (with the exception of the Seventh Day Adventists), and the Episcopal Church of America has expressed its official approval of it in the strongest terms.

Although the Anglican Church did not echo the approval of its American counterpart 'in the strongest terms', there could be no doubt of its attitude of general approval as stated by the Archbishop of Canterbury when he rose also to support Lord Merthyr's Motion. He said that he had 'no great belief in the value of uniformity as such', but added:

'Constitutionally, I have a great dislike of any proposal to change long and well-established customs unless there is very strong reason; but I am bound to say that I have found it impossible to resist the plea for reform in this matter, which comes, I think it may be said, with practical unanimity from the representatives of all the great organizations of trade, industry and commerce throughout the civilized world.

'The matter has been complicated, as noble Lords have pointed out, by its immense complexities, including the vagaries of the moon, and it is something, at any rate, in the way of bringing order into this confusion that the League of Nations committee—oddly enough described as 'Transit and Communications'—have sufficiently cleared the issue to put two alternatives before— it may be said—the world: the alternatives of the equal months or the equal quarters.

'I express no opinion as to the merits of these two alternatives, but I associate myself with everything that has been said by the noble Lord on the importance of the undertaking of this section of the League of Nations, the Transit Section, to give a definite recommendation, after consulting with all the experts who are available, as to which of the two plans it recommends. I think it would be a real misfortune if this matter were allowed to drift on beyond October this year when it could not be fruitfully considered again until 1940'.

After discussing the position of the Roman and Ortho-dox Churches in regard to the Easter controversy, the Archbishop concluded: '. . . if this country gives a strong lead to the League of Nations Transit Section to come to some decision between these two alternative schemes of calendar reform, and if in October of this year the Quad-rennial Conference can register a general agreement on this matter among most of the principal communions of the world, then I hope it may be possible for the Vatican to reconsider its hitherto generally-expressed attitude. If so, then I hope that my noble friend Lord Desborough may be still alive to see the fruition of his long labours!'

Unfortunately, Lord Desborough did not live to see it, nor could he have been greatly encouraged at the end of this debate, for much cold water was poured on the aspirations of all calendar reform proponents by the Earl of Feversham, who replied for the Government, and stressed that an official British Committee of Inquiry set up under Lord Burnham in 1930 had found little demand in the country for reform, and not very much interest in the subject. 'In those circumstances', he concluded, 'the Government feel that they cannot go to the lengths which some of those who have taken part in the debate to-day would wish them to go'.

The time was, in fact, not yet ripe!

Already when the war began the calendar reform question had faded out of prominence. With the excite-of the war—even the period of 'phoney' war—it could not compete. There set in another term of non-interest on the part both of Press and public. In America, of course, the campaign went on and the faithful *Journal of Calendar Reform* continued to be published by the World Calendar Association in New York and copies to be circulated over here, but it was mainly preaching to the converted. Very rarely an article appeared in the English Press—the present author wrote one in *Caval-*

cade, a then popular news-review magazine, in January 1944—but on the whole the subject was shelved, apparently for the duration. All the more surprising therefore that it spurted up again when the late Admiral Beamish made his gallant effort to generate some action in the matter in the House of Commons in March 1944.[1]

On Rear Admiral T. P. H. Beamish, M.P., had fallen the mantle of Lord Desborough, that leading light of the earlier years of the calendar campaign. His was almost a lone voice speaking in the wilderness, and we have seen with what near derision it was received. Yet there was reason to expect a very different reception. This was a supreme moment when, with Government imagination, a valuable contribution might have been made to national efficiency, to put it no higher. The occasion was not incomparable with the time during World War I when Daylight Saving was introduced, as a measure for increasing industrial and war output and reducing avoidable waste. That proposal had been a subject of ridicule for years, but it turned out in the event to be one of the most beneficent readjustments of time that human ingenuity had devised—an annual boon to millions, costing nothing. In just the same way, the rationalising of the calendar at that period of utmost productive stress would have increased efficiency and consequently output, if only by saving the time of those whose job it was to work out the complicated schedules of production and keep the complex and multifarious war account. Who is to say that it might not even have brought the war sooner to an end? It certainly could have helped.

The opportunity passed. Another long period of apathy set in. It would have lasted until now except for the imaginative and public-spirited interest of two men, one English, the other Welsh. These were James Avery Joyce, a London barrister, and Lord Merthyr. Mr. Joyce is now honorary secretary of the British Section

[1] *Debate in Parliament*, Part II, Chapter 8.

of the World Calendar Association, Lord Merthyr its chairman. This group was formed in May, 1952.

It is worth noting that both men had much earlier been convinced of the need for the reform of the calendar. J. Avery Joyce, who had a long experience of international movements and who for ten years had been chairman of a British group of educationalists formed in 1939 under the title of the World Unity Movement (later the World Citizenship Movement), was particularly attracted by the Worldsday device as a means of symbolizing and developing the essential unity of the human race. His intimate knowledge of the work of the League of Nations at Geneva had brought him in touch with calendar reform between the wars.

In Merthyr's case it was the advantages of the Cotsworth thirteen-month plan which first attracted his support. In this respect he agreed with Lord Desborough and supported him both in his campaign for a fixed Easter and for a reformed thirteen-month calendar. It was Lord Merthyr who had taken up the case in the House of Lords in 1936 and had in his turn been supported by Desborough; it was he also who made a powerful though unsuccessful appeal in the same House in 1951 for the amendment of the Easter Act of 1928 so that it might then be put into operation.

His view still is that the thirteen-month plan would offer the better solution, *if it were practical*, but since he recognizes that the immense dislocation and confusion which its adoption would entail render it impractical, he underwrites wholeheartedly the World Calendar proposal on the grounds that it is the most practical reform yet put forward. Thus he has long been an important, and is now the principal, representative of the calendar reform movement, and in particular the World Calendar school, in Britain.

Early in 1952 the two met to discuss the possibility of reviving public interest in the subject, and the outcome

was an invitation to a number of eminent men and
women to a meeting in a committee room of the House
of Lords on May 6 1952, to consider the matter. The
response was sufficiently satisfactory to justify the
formation of a committee, which was thereupon formed.
Deciding to devote itself exclusively to advocacy of the
World Calendar, it became the British Section of the
World Calendar Association, International, of New
York. A number of influential personalities known to be
interested were invited to join an Advisory Board, and
the strength of its appeal is indicated by the width of
interests of the list of some of the Board's members, such
as Sir Adrian Boult, Lord Crook, Peter Freeman, M.P.,
Miss Ruth Fry, E. H. Garner-Evans, M.P., Professor
Lancelot Hogben, F.R.S., Lord Mathers, I. J. Pitman,
M.P., Henry Usborne, M.P. and Dr. L. E. C. Hughes.

Among the keenest British advocates of the World
Calendar is no less an authority on time than the
Astronomer Royal, Sir Harold Spencer Jones. One of
the first steps the committee took in its new campaign
was an invitation to the Astronomer Royal to lecture on
the subject. Under the auspices of the Royal Society of
Arts, Sir Harold read an extremely interesting Paper on
'The Calendar, Past, Present and Future', in the
Society's lecture hall in London, in which he showed the
World Calendar to be a logical historical development
and advocated its urgent adoption. This, and a further
Paper on 'A Reformed Calendar' given by Lord Merthyr
at the same place, received wide newspaper publicity
and can be said to have re-awakened general interest in
the subject. Both addresses have since been published.[1]
Lectures have also been given in various towns, meetings
held, and explanatory literature issued on current aspects
of the problem; all of which have done much to stimulate
a wider interest in Britain.

[1] World Calendar Pamphlets Nos. 2 and 3, 20 Buckingham Street,
London, W.C.2.

CHAPTER VII

Where the Nations Stand

IF ONE SURVEYS the vast agglomeration of approval of the principle of calendar reform, or even the imposing array of expressed support for the World Calendar, it is hard to understand why so simple and beneficial a revision has not been carried out, after thirty years of intense study and activity. Probably the answer lies in the deep entrenchment of habit, and the fact that there is nothing essentially dramatic about the calendar. It is one of those ordinary everyday things, requiring no instant action. People are interested—but not enough to put themselves out about it.

A neat statement of just this was made by no less a personage than the man destined shortly afterwards to reach the highest peak of eminence as President of the United States of America. On April 11 1935, Senator Harry S. Truman, of Missouri, writing officially on the stationery of the United States Senate (Committee of Appropriations), addressed the following letter to Mr. C. D. Morris, editor of the *Journal of Calendar Reform*:

Dear Mr. Morris:
Replying to yours of the eighth instant, regarding the revised calendar, of course all of us are interested in the revision of the calendar as something to talk about as an academic matter, and personally I would like to see it go into effect.

However, I have never given the matter serious thought or study because it would take a Pope Gregory the Great or a Julius Cæsar to put these changes into effect.

Sincerely,
HARRY S. TRUMAN.

It might well be said that if any man ever had the opportunity to convert 'academic interest' into practical interest, that man was President Truman; but one can also admit that he had other things to attend to. . . .

Yet Mr. Truman's view was, and probably still is, that of nine out of ten of all intelligent people. He 'would like to see it come into effect', but. . . . There is so often a 'but', usually meaning 'I can't be bothered to take any personal action'.

On the whole there can be no doubt that opinion favours reform. Overwhelmingly, where the subject has been studied, that reform takes the shape of the World Calendar project. If so far it has not been successful in achieving its object, the World Calendar Association has at least brought out clearly the desirability of action and has provided a very considerable framework. It has created, or been largely responsible for the development of, calendar reform organizations in no fewer than thirty-six other countries, all of which are working to promote adoption of the World Calendar by their own governments, or with the wider view of its world employment.[1]

Some of these groups, as might be expected, are more active than others, but in the sum their work represents a powerful movement. For the last six years most of them have sent representatives to an annual meeting of the World Calendar Association International, an organization which exists as a non-profit-making body under a U.S. Charter. At its 1953 meeting there were represented affiliated organizations from:

Argentina	Great Britain	Peru
Australia	Greece	Philippines
Belgium	Japan	Salvador
Canada	Mexico	Spain
China	Nicaragua	Switzerland
Cuba	Norway	Uruguay
France	Panama	United States

[1] See Appendix B.

in addition to which reports were received from India, Eire, the Netherlands, New Zealand and Sweden.[1]

So it could not be said that the nucleus, the foundation on which to build action, is anywhere wanting. The world advisory committee of the Association comprises fifty-one members, all eminent in their respective countries in scientific, social, religious or some other field.

At this particular meeting, Miss Achelis, who is President as well as founder, summarized the activities of 1952. The most active organizations in the cause, she said, were those of Canada, France, Britain, Japan, Panama, and Switzerland. In Canada the standing of calendar reform had advanced to the stage of government approval and Canadian delegates would be found on the side of the World Calendar wherever and whenever the subject might come up for discussion. In France, the distinguished Abbé Chauve-Bertrand was an enthusiastic supporter, and renewed interest had been shown through the leadership of M. Albert Caquot, head of AFNOR, the Association Francaise de Normalisation, who had lately spent a month in the United States in connection with the triennial convention of the International Organization for Standardization. This latter organization, in Switzerland, was strongly on the side of the new calendar, and was making an energetic effort to rally its members in their various countries to this cause. Japan had just published the first two of a series of impressive monographs on calendar reform, and Panama had shown similar enterprise in an 84-page booklet in Spanish, issued by the chairman Juan Rivera Reyes. Similar reports of more or less vigorous activity came from other countries.

Of the members of the United Nations Organization, seventeen are now recorded as having formally accepted the principle of the World Calendar and stand ready to

[2] *Journal of Calendar Reform*, March 1953.

put it into operation when there is hope of majority agreement. Unfortunately the number does not include any of the great powers, though this might largely be explained by the fact that the bigger they are, the harder to move; and it is all too easy to say, as the British Government says, that 'the time is not ripe'.

Although it is clear that in many parts of the world there is approval, even governmental approval, and immense support from influential individuals and organizations, it is a reform which only international, not to say universal action, can bring about. Hence the key to success lies obviously in discussion within the U.N. Organization. It is here that the voice of Britain should be heard. With a lead from either Britain or the United States it is reasonable to expect that a majority of nations would welcome the reform.

The same no doubt applies to the U.S.S.R. And while there has been, within the writer's knowledge, no report of opinion on the subject from behind the Iron Curtain, it is reasonable to believe that the country which has made the boldest calendar experiments in the last century would be favourably disposed towards adopting a new revision so conspicuously beneficial from the point of view of industrial efficiency.

The writer indeed believes that if it were again officially brought forward, the U.S.S.R. would not be antagonistic. At the same time it must be admitted that that country was one of the three, the others being France and the United States, which moved for postponement of the question when, at the fourth session of the Economic and Social Council of the U.N. in March 1947, the delegation from Peru had submitted a draft resolution for the adoption in 1950 of 'a new calendar on the basis of the plan prepared by the World Calendar Association'. Supporting Peru for immediate discussion in that instance were China and Norway, but in view of pressure of international affairs the Noes had it, and the

Council decided to adjourn the matter. At the same time they called for a dossier of the whole subject to be prepared for full-dress deliberation the next time opportunity should arise for its consideration.

This, of course, was designed to carry forward to the new United Nations the valiant work of the old League of Nations. Mr. Trygve Lie took it in hand, and by the time the question arose again, not before the Economic and Social Council but before the General Committee, two years later, he had produced a brief but valuable review of the whole subject, ably and judicially balanced, putting *pros* and *cons* with admirable impartiality. It led inevitably to a re-statement of the World Calendar case, and since it comes from so eminently reliable and unprejudiced an examiner, it is worth quoting at the cost perhaps of some little repetition. The pertinent section was that numbered 'V', as follows:

V. Consequences and Problems Relating to the Adoption of the World Calendar[1]

The advantages usually emphasized by those in favour of the reform of the calendar are as follows:

Since 'The World Calendar' is perpetual, all years would be identical except for the supplementary day in leap years and it, therefore, has all the advantages of a fixed calendar.

Its method of dividing the year into four equal and identical quarters makes it possible to use the quarter as a unit of subdivision, which is very convenient for certain aspects of everyday life.

With the existence of this calendar, statistical surveys, budgetary estimates, financial operations and plans for economic and social organizations may be drawn up in a much simpler fashion. Comparisons between any two periods may be drawn with simpler calculations and fixed formulæ.

Furthermore, periodic events, such as the convening of a Parliament, can be permanently fixed as to both the date and the day of the week.

[1] U.N. Document E/465, July 14 1947, and others—quoted by *Journal of Calendar Reform* 1947 (translated by the Editor).

The stability of the calendar also makes it possible to contemplate the stabilization of festivals which are at present movable.

It must be noted that this reform would, to a great extent, meet the need of improving the measurement of time from the economic and social point of view.

On the contrary, those opposed to the reform emphasize the following disadvantages among others: 'The World Calendar' shares with all calendar reforms the disadvantage that the alteration introduced will necessitate certain calculations in order to find equivalents between the new dates and the dates of the former system. Moreover, the fact that in 'The World Calendar' Sunday does not always correspond to the real day of the Sabbath may cause practical difficulties for extremely orthodox worshippers of certain denominations. Nevertheless, this disadvantage only affects a very small part of the population of the world.

On the other hand, the adoption of the draft resolution raises certain procedural problems and practical difficulties. From the international point of view, the reform cannot be adopted to any advantage if a certain number of governments do not introduce it into their legislatures. In this connection, the House of Representatives of the United States Congress has already received the draft of H.R.1345, to authorize the President of the United States to take the necessary measures for the adoption of 'The World Calendar' on 1 January 1950. If a vote is taken upon this draft, it will facilitate the adoption of the reform throughout the world.

It seems that of all the calendars studied on the international plane, the draft submitted to the Economic and Social Council by the Delegation of Peru is the one which has received the most favourable comments.

The draft submitted by the Delegation of Peru (E/291) emphasizes that 1 January 1950 is from many points of view the most suitable date for the transition from the Gregorian calendar to the new calendar, and that the adoption of 'The World Calendar' makes it essential that legislative and administrative measures should be taken in time; the draft, therefore, recommends that the Economic and Social Council instruct an *ad hoc* committee to study the proposed reform with a view to making definite proposals and pronouncing on this subject.

That was a very fair statement, and together with the other material of the Secretary-General's memorandum projected the matter clearly. It was ready for discussion with more and readier facts at any future committee's finger-tips than had been available when Peru had raised the subject. Perhaps its postponement at that moment, though disappointing, had been all for the best. But in the following year, 1948, no delegation raised the question. However, it came up again the year after that.

It was on May 27 1949, that the *New York Herald Tribune* announced that 'Panama has proposed to the United Nations that the world shelve its calendar and adopt one that will remain identical from year to year.

'In a memorandum released today', the newspaper continued, 'the Panamanian delegation asked discussion of a "World Calendar" to be placed on the agenda of the next session of the General Assembly in the interests of general harmony and stability. Prompt action by the U.N. was urged as the change-over could readily be made on 31 December 1950 when the Gregorian and World Calendars coincide.

'If no action is taken at the fourth session of the Assembly, the memorandum concluded, "such a fortuitous opportunity for calendar reform will not recur until 1956, resulting in six more years of avoidable calendar chaos"'.

Again it had been one of the South American countries that had made the move. Now the matter had reached the highest level. Now it was likely to come before the august General Assembly of United Nations. Now, it seemed—for there was no common-sense reason why it should not—now, it seemed, at last the matter would be thrashed out in the light of all the necessities, and the conclusion would be inevitable that the beneficent World Calendar should be adopted as a new civil calendar in all countries, starting in 1950 when the two calendars would coincide and the innovation could be introduced without inconvenience. So its proponents argued.

But there is many a slip. . . .

At the New York office of the Association there was joyful anticipation of success, a success which it was not doubted would mark the end of an unremitting nineteen-years' campaign for this essentially simple—but in achievement, oh, how difficult!—reform. Hope ran high. The third quarterly issue of the *Journal* for that year was published as an enlarged special United Nations number. In between the first announcement of the hearing and publication it had made as thorough a survey as possible of the attitude of all the member nations to the calendar question, and a summary of these was printed.

'In September', it said in its leading article, 'the United Nations has a golden opportunity to correct existing "calendar-chaos" by adopting the World Calendar. The issue, being non-political, non-sectarian and of paramount exigency, holding immense benefits for all nations, races, creeds and peoples, offers an unrivalled possibility for unanimous approval of Member States'.

It then listed its summary of opinion. 'As we go to press', it reported, 'the results of an unofficial poll, taken by an interested delegation, of information direct from chancelleries and delegations reveals the following attitude on the World Calendar resolution:

Favourable:

Argentina	El Salvador	Nicaragua
Australia	Ethiopia	Norway
Belgium	France	Panama
Bolivia	Greece	Paraguay
Brazil	Guatemala	Peru
Canada	Haiti	Philippines
Chile	Honduras	Saudi Arabia
Colombia	Iran	Sweden

Costa Rica	Iraq	Turkey
Cuba	Israel	United Kingdom[1]
Denmark	Liberia	U.S.A.[1]
Dominican	Luxembourg	Uruguay
Republic	Mexico	Venezuela[1]
Ecuador	Netherlands	Yugoslavia
Egypt	New Zealand	

Without Instructions:

Afghanistan	India	Ukraine
Bylorussia	Lebanon	Union of South
Burma	Pakistan	Africa
China	Poland	U.S.S.R.
Czechoslovakia	Siam	Yeman
Iceland	Syria	

Against:
None.

'Since Afghanistan, China,[2] Czechoslovakia and Syria have previously approved and supported the World Calendar', the report continued, 'it is reasonable to assume that their opinions will remain unchanged in the matter. Therefore these four countries, at present listed as "without instructions" will in all probability vote affirmatively.

'Hence the status of the World Calendar resolution shapes up at this time:

47 *Favourable Nations*,
12 *Without Instructions*.

'With an indicated favourable vote of 47—more than two-thirds of the States Members of the United Nations, which majority is required to pass the desired resolution in the General Assembly—it would appear that chances are excellent for the world finally to have a perpetual time system as of the last day of 1950.'

[1] If there is a majority of opinion evidenced.
[2] The China here referred to is necessarily Nationalist China.

The Association's jubilation seemed justified. Even allowing for one or two doubtful starters classified among the 'favourables'—and their inclusion may quite possibly have been a little optimistic—there appeared still to be a safe majority. At the worst, governments would have been called on to give the matter mature consideration with a view to final decision. The *Journal* concluded its leader with the expectant phrase: 'Here's to Success!'

But success was not yet.

The next issue of the *Journal of Calendar Reform* told the sad story.

'The afternoon of 21 September 1949', it wrote, 'may prove to be a costly one for all the world. For on this date there was imposed on the world, or at least on a large part of it, a heavy six-year handicap—the carrying of a financial burden, namely, the outmoded unreliable present-day calendar.

'It was during this fateful afternoon that the newly-constituted fourteen-nation General Committee of the United Nations assembled to determine the agenda for the Fourth Regular Session of the General Assembly. Interest ran high as 72 items were provisionally presented—many of which were controversial and internationally complicated.

'One by one, "bones of contention" were considered, and either included or withdrawn in rapid-fire order, establishing a record for General Committee action. It soon appeared as though all controversial items had been handled and delegates' rhetoric exhausted. A momentary quiet blanketed the room.

'Breaking this lull, the President intoned: "Shall we then include all other items on the agenda?"—or words to that effect.

'A rustle of papers by Senator Warren Austin of the United States Delegation focused eyes on him as he proposed through his microphone that item No. 60, on the plan for the reform of the calendar presented by Panama, be postponed to a later session.

' "But why?" the delegates wanted to know.

'(*There should be some reason of paramount importance for postponing action on a matter involving savings of millions of dollars for every nation. Especially is this true in view of the present international monetary situation.*)[1]

' "Overcrowded agenda," came the answer.

'Panama, not a member of the committee of fourteen, but privileged to speak as the proposer, ably stated that a full agenda could not be properly advanced as a reason for postponement as it could not be expected that the agenda would be otherwise than crowded.

'Chile interposed that various delegations had wanted the merits of Calendar Reform discussed for several years, but met with a refusal.

'Then came the vote, resulting in a four-to-four tie, and by the Chairman's ruling discussion of the item was deferred. A simple majority was needed to obtain action at this session.

'Thus the benefit of the nations' obtaining a wide cross-section of opinion through discussion of this measure, designed to relieve the peoples of the world from the annoyances and wastefulness of the present irregular, unstable calendar, has been lost—or at least postponed.

'The vote showed the Philippines supporting the United States, joined by the United Kingdom and Denmark. Voting for discussion of the item of Calendar Reform at this session were Canada, China, Chile and Venezuela. Abstaining were the U.S.S.R., Poland, Pakistan and Brazil. Greece and France were absent.

'Did the affirmative voting nations know that they would save millions by the adoption of a perpetual time system?

[1] *Journal's* italics and brackets.

'Did lack of similar economic foresight and knowledge cause the request for postponement?

'Is there a moral to this story?

'Only that the provisional agenda was not one-tenth as overburdened as are the shoulders of American and other national taxpayers. It's highly possible that they may demand a few answers to the delaying tactics on a subject holding such potentialities for financial relief, as well as great social benefits to mankind generally.

'At least they may raise their mighty voices and insist on an opportunity to have the *merits* and *adoption* of calendar reform discussed and weighed at the next session of the United Nations—for huge economic savings can be made a very powerful persuader.

'In the meantime, to quote His Excellency Dr. Ricardo J. Alfaro, of Panama: "We have lost a battle, but we have not lost the war. We shall continue the fight." '

Thus the headquarters of this now world-wide movement took its great disappointment bravely and not uncheerfully, and looked forward to fighting another day. Their optimistic hope that the subject would automatically come up again the following year, however, was not to be realized, nor was it brought forward officially again until in October 1953 the Indian Permanent Representative to the U.N. made his formal request for it to be included in the agenda of the eighteenth session of the Economic and Social Council in 1954. Moreover, the feature of the affair which in New York must have been most galling after so long a campaign was the fact that the obstruction which had defeated their hopes had come from their own nation. It had been the United States delegate, Warren Austin, who had put the wedge under the wheel of progress.

True, there had been a crowded agenda; but all such agendas are crowded. Could there have been in the Senator's mind an antipathy to the World Calendar and a sympathy for some other? Only the Senator knows, but we have seen how the issue in America has been confused.

Now the sights had to be raised on a more distant target. The opportunity for a change in 1950 had passed. The next convenient dates for adoption would be January 1 1956, and January 1 1961, the next occasions when again the old and the new calendars would coincide at the start of a year. The Association at once proclaimed a five-year plan with the 1956 target in view.

They may realize it.

If patience, persistence and hard work in a good cause count as they should, they will.

S

United Nations Economic and Social Council

EXTRACT FROM 'Communication dated October 28 from the Permanent Representative of India to the United Nations to the Secretary-General' circulated October 30 1953.[1]

MEMORANDUM ON THE QUESTION OF WORLD CALENDAR REFORM

I

The ideal of the whole world is to have a logical and perpetual calendar to replace the present Gregorian Calendar, because it is widely recognized that the calendar we now use is unsatisfactory for the economic, social, educational, scientific and other activities of man. Modern progress demands the change.

Such a revision has been the subject of study and research on the part of experts, institutions and international organisations for many years. The consensus of opinion is that a new time system is necessary, adhering to the customary twelve months; but that it should be uniform; an invariable calendar, perpetually the same, more regular, scientific and advantageous from every point of view than the present Gregorian Calendar.

II

Our present Calendar is to all intents and purposes, the same as that introduced by Julius Caesar in 45 B.C. which, due to its irregularity and the time difference caused by erroneous length of the year, was corrected and re-adjusted in 1582 by Pope Gregory XIII.

[1] E/2514 Annex English, Page 2.

The divisions in the Gregorian Calendar of year, months, quarters and half-years are of unequal length, the months being from twenty-eight to thirty-one days. As a result, the number of days in the four quarters are, respectively, ninety (ninety-one in a leap year), ninety-one, ninety-two and ninety-two. As a result, again, the first half-year, contains two or three days less than the second. The number of weeks in the quarters and half-years is also unequal. There is consequently considerable confusion and uncertainty in economic dealings and in the preparation and analysis of statistics and accounts. The comparability of salaries, interest, insurance, pensions, leases and rent of one period of the year with another is greatly vitiated due to the unequal length of months which have from 24 to 27 weekdays plus Sundays.

Further, the calendar is not fixed and changes each year. The year, in fact, consists of fifty-two weeks plus one or two days. Thus, if the first day of the year is a Sunday, in the following year it is a Monday (or even a Tuesday in the case of a leap year). The exact reproduction of the calendar of any year only takes place once every twenty-eight years. Thus, the day of the month falls each year on a different day of the week from the one on which it fell the previous year.

Consequently, the dates of periodical events can never be fixed with precision. Such a date can in fact, only be determined in two ways: either by the day of the month (August 15, for example) or by the day of the week in the month (the third Tuesday in October). If the day of the month is fixed for periodical events, this day may sometimes fall on a Sunday or general holiday. Each year the authorities have, therefore, to make a special decision, as for instance for the meeting of a tribunal, the convocation of Parliament, the dates of holidays, fairs, markets, the fixing of summer-time, etc. On the other hand, if a special day (the first Monday in the month, for example) is fixed for these events, other difficulties arise, as the date corresponding to this day varies continually from month to month and from year to year. If the calendar were fixed, the dates of these events could be fixed once and for all. They would fall on the same dates as well as on the same days of the week.

The greatest drawback from a statistical and commercial point of view is that, since the various days of the week are not of the same value as regards volume of trade, and the years and the months do not from year to year include the same number of individual weekdays, there can be no genuine statistical comparison between one year and another, while the various subdivisions of the year itself—the half-years, quarters and months —are likewise incapable of comparison.

III

The proposed scheme of the World Calendar has overcome all the above drawbacks of the present Gregorian Calendar. It is scientific, uniform, stable and perpetual with but one unvarying calendar every year. It retains the present 12 months; thus the four quarters are always equal; each quarter has 3 months, 13 weeks, or 91 days, beginning on Sunday and ending on Saturday; each month contains an exact number of 26 working days *plus* Sundays; and days and dates always agree from year to year, and holidays are permanently fixed. The calendar remains identical from year to year. It offers harmony and order to all strata of society-government, finance, industry, labour, retail trade, administration of justice, home life, transportation and education. All statistics compiled on the basis of a month, a quarter or a year are strictly comparable with one another.

IV

The 365th day of the year in the World Calendar is proposed to be an international holiday, without any weekday name, dedicated simultaneously in every country of the world to the universal harmony and unity of mankind, thus knitting all races, creeds, peoples and nations into a closer bond of fellowship, creating world-wide citizenship in the "One World'. The potentialities of 'Worldsday' for strengthening and promoting international peace among all nations are of great value.

In leap years another similar international holiday is interposed between June 30 and July 1.

V

The only feasible time for adopting a new calendar is when both the old and the new calendars coincide, enabling the change-over to be instituted with a minimum of disturbance. Both the outgoing Gregorian and the incoming World Calendars coincide on Sunday, January 1 1956, giving the nations of the world two years' time to prepare for this significant and historical reform if adopted by the United Nations now.

VI

The subject of Calendar Reform has been exhaustively studied by the United Nations Secretariat as shown in a report by the Secretary-General in document E/465, dated July 14 1947. It gives the entire history of the movement and the progress made up to that time. The report concludes that the proposal 'is the plan which has received the most favourable comments'.

The World Calendar Association International

Affiliates and National Organizations

ARGENTINA: The World Calendar Association, International, Affiliate, Guillermo Mascarenhas, Chairman, Corientes 655, Buenos Aires.

AUSTRALIA: The World Calendar Association, International, Affiliate, H. J. M. Abraham, Chairman, Commonwealth Observatory, Canberra.

BELGIUM: The World Calendar Association, International, Affiliate, Professor M. Déhalu, Chairman, 17 Quai du Halage, Visé.

BOLIVIA: Comité Boliviano del Calendario Mundial, Dr. Gaston Barrera, Chairman, La Paz University, La Paz.

BRAZIL: The World Calendar Association, International, Affiliate, Rear Admiral Radler de Aquino (Ret.), Chairman, Rua Raul Pompeia No. 133, Rio de Janeiro.

CANADA: The World Calendar Association, International, Affiliate, A. J. Hills, Chairman, Room 31, 102 Bank St., Ottawa.

CHILE: Comité Chileno del Calendario Mundial, Prof. Alberto Cumming, Chairman, Calle Manuel Rodriguez, Santiago.

CHINA: The World Calendar Association, International, Affiliate, Dr. Ch'ing-Sung Yü, Honorary President; Dr. Chu Chia-hua, Chairman, 15 Chuan Chow St., Taipeh, Taiwan.

COLOMBIA: Comité Colombiano del Calendario Mundial, Dr. Belisario Ruiz Wilches, Chairman, Observatorio Astronomico Nacional, Apartado No. 2584, Bogotá.

COSTA RICA: The World Calendar Association, International, Affiliate, Don José Borrase, Chairman, 'LaPrensa Libre', Aptdo. Postal 1533, San José.

CUBA: The World Calendar Association, International, Affiliate, Dr. Elias Entralgo, Chairman, Havana University, Havana; Dr. Salvador Massip, Adviser.

DOMINICAN REPUBLIC: The World Calendar Association, International, Affiliate, Barney N. Morgan, Chairman, Box 727, Ciudad Trujillo.

ECUADOR: The World Calendar Association, International, Affiliate, Dr. Rafael H. Elizalde, Honorary President; Dr. Jorge Egred P., Chairman, Astronomical Observatory, Apartado 165, Quito.

FRANCE: The World Calendar Association, International, Affiliate, Senateur Justin Godart, President; Paul-Louis Hervier, Chairman, 5, Rue Bernoulli, Paris.

GREAT BRITAIN: The World Calendar Association, British Section, Lord Merthyr, Chairman; J. Avery Joyce, Honorary Secretary, 20 Buckingham St., London W.C.2.

GREECE: The World Calendar Association, International, Affiliate, Athanase Politis, Chairman; Prof. S. Plakidis, Secy., Observatory of University of Athens.

GUATEMALA: The World Calendar Association, International, Affiliate, Don Manuel Eduardo Rodriguez, Chairman, Diario 'El Imparcial', Guatemala.

HONDURAS: The World Calendar Association, International, Affiliate, Don Julio Lozano, H. E. Don Rafael Heliodoro Valle, Honorary Presidents: Ingeniero Miguel Angel Ramos, Chairman, Biblioteca Nacional, Tegucigalpa.

INDIA: Committee on Calendar Reform, Prof. M. N. Saha, 92, Upper Circular Road, Calcutta.

ITALY: Italian National Committee on Calendar Reform, Prof. Amedeo Giannini, Secy., Via del Seminario, 113, Rome.

JAPAN: The World Calendar Association, International, Affiliate, Dr. Joe Ueta, President; Dr. Susumu Imoto, Secretary, Osaka Municipal Planetarium, Yotsubashi, Nishiku, Osaka.

MEXICO: The World Calendar Association, International, Affiliate, Dr. Joaquín Gallo, Honorary President; Dr. Horacio Herrera, Chairman, Sociedad de Estudios Astronómicos y Geofísicos, Av. Observatorio No. 192, Tacubaya, D.F.

NEW ZEALAND: The World Calendar Association, International, Affiliate, Dr. I. L. Thomsen, Chairman, Carter Observatory, Wellington, W.1.

NICARAGUA: The World Calendar Association, International, Affiliate, Don José H. Montalvan, Chairman, Palacio Nacional, Managua.

NORWAY: The World Calendar Association, International, Affiliate, Major K. S. Klingenberg, Chairman, Thomas Heftyes Gate, 56B, Oslo.

PANAMA: The World Calendar Association, International, Affiliate, Dr. Juan Rivera Reyes, Chairman, Panama City.

PARAGUAY: Comité Paraguayano del Calendario Mundial, H. E. Señor Ministro Coronel Don Luis Irrazabal, Chairman, Paraguayan Embassy, Lima, Peru.

PERU: The World Calendar Association, International, Affiliate, Don Luis Montero y Tirado, Chairman, Av. Uruguay 305, Lima.

PHILLIPPINES: The World Calendar Association, International, Affiliate, Ramon Caro, Chairman, 116 Padre Faura, Manila.

SALVADOR: The World Calendar Association, International, Affiliate, Don Napoleon Viera Altamirano, Chairman, 'El Diario de Hoy', San Salvador.

SPAIN: The World Calendar Association, International, Affiliate, Rev. Father Antonio Romañá, S.J., Honorary President; Ramon Ximenez Gil de Avalle, Chairman, Urgel, 44·1° 4ª, Barcelona.

SWITZERLAND: The World Calendar Association, International, Affiliate, Prof. Emile Marchand, Chmn., 2, Genferstasse, Zurich.

TURKEY: The World Calendar Association, International, Affiliate, Dr. I. A. Dereoglu, Chairman, Beyoglu, Istiklal Caddesi 485, Istanbul.

UNITED STATES: The World Calendar Association, Inc., Elisabeth Achelis, President, 630 Fifth Avenue, New York 20.

URUGUAY: The World Calendar Association, International, Affiliate, Prof. Alberto Reyes Thévenet, Chairman, Liceo 'Hector Miranda', Calle Sierra 2274, Montevideo.

YUGOSLAVIA: Yugoslavian Committee on Calendar Reform. (Without a Chairman due to the death of Mr. George Curchin.)

Other Affiliates are in process of organization in Eire and South Africa.

Index

Accountants, Chartered, 162
Achelis, Elisabeth, 92, 143, 149, 153, 218, 239
Acland, Sir Richard, 131, 132
Act of 1752, 57, 70
Afghanistan, 155, 257
Alaska, 203
Albania, 135
Alexander the Great, 1, 2
Alfaro, Dr. Ricardo J., 260
American Statistical Society, 169
Anglican Church (*see* Churches)
Anno Mundi, definition of, 2
Apathy, British, 148, 156, 168, 238, 242
Arabia, 118, 256
Argentina, 148, 155, 250, 256, 266
Armelin, Gustav, 89, 127, 151
Armstrong, Charles E., 180
Ashburgh, Lewis E., 150
Association of Normalisation, 169, 251
Assyrian Calendar (*see* Calendar)
Astronomical date, 179
Astronomical Union, International, 82, 92, 93, 95, 134
Astronomer Royal, 118, 121
A.U.C., definition of, 41
Austin, Senator Warren, 258, 260
Australia, 155, 250, 256, 266
Austria, 156
Aztecs, 4, 30

Baar, Armand, 135
Babylon, 2
Babylonian Calendar (*see* Calendar)
Bacon, Roger, 46
Baire, R., 107, 108
Basle, Council of, 47
Baume-Pluvinel, M. de la, 135
B.B.C., 162
Beamish, Rear-Admiral T. P. H., M.P., 157, 246
Bedeus, Baron Gustav, 104
Belgium, 250, 256, 266
Bellamy, H. S., 15, 30
Bigourdain, G., 95, 134
Birthdays, 62, 68, 70, 166
Bolivia (*see also* Tiahuanaco), 256, 266

Booth, Willis H., 95
Boult, Sir Adrian, 248
Bradley, Dr. James, 51, 56, 60, 198
Brazil, 149, 155, 256, 259, 266
Brinton, Dr. D. G., 31
Bristol riots, 63
Bulgaria, 156
Bureau d'Etudes, 242
Burma, 257
Burnham, Lord, 245
Bylorussia, 257

Cabrol, Right Rev. Fernand, 243
Cæsar, Augustus, 10
Cæsar, Julius, 10, 25, 84, 134
Calendar
    Application to industry, 186 ff.
    Assyrian, 23
    Aztec (*see* Aztecs)
    Babylonian, 23
    Chinese, 21, 26, 27
    Decimal, 226 (*see also* Calendar, French Revolutionary)
    Defects, 11, 145, 193
    Defects (13-month), 145, 146
    Earliest, 14 ff., 21
    Edwards (*see* Edwards Calendar)
    Effects on travel, etc., 13
    Egyptian, 21
    Elements of, 7
    Freakish, 102
    French Revolutionary, 5, 84 ff., 102, 104
    Gateway of Tianhuanaco (*see* Tahuanaco, *also* picture facing page 72)
    Greek, 1, 6, 24, 139
    Gregorian, 4, 8, 9
        Introduction in Europe, 48, 71
        Introduction in Britain, 50 ff.
    Inca (*see* Incas)
    Indian, 21, 27, 96, 153, 156, 277 ff.
    Japanese, 27
    Jewish, 8, 21, 43
    Julian (*see* Julian Calendar)
    Mayan, 34
    Mahommedan, 8, 117 ff., 133
    Ninety-nine year, 195, 196 (set out)

269